Care and Restoration

Care and Restoration of Barometers

Philip R. Collins

Baros Books

First published 1990. Reprinted 1993, 1999

Baros Books
5 Victoria Road
Trowbridge
Wiltshire
BA14 7LH

British Library Cataloguing in Publication Data

Collins, Philip R.
    Care and Restoration of Barometers.
    1. Barometers. Restoration. Maintenance & Repair.
    I. Title
    681′.2

ISBN   0-948382-05-8

Typesetting by Datalink Typesettng & Graphics, 6/8 Cotterel Court, Monmouth Place, Bath.
Illustrations screened by Norton Photo Litho, New Pitt Cottages, Paulton, Bristol.
Printed and bound by Cromwell Press, Trowbridge, Wiltshire.

Contents

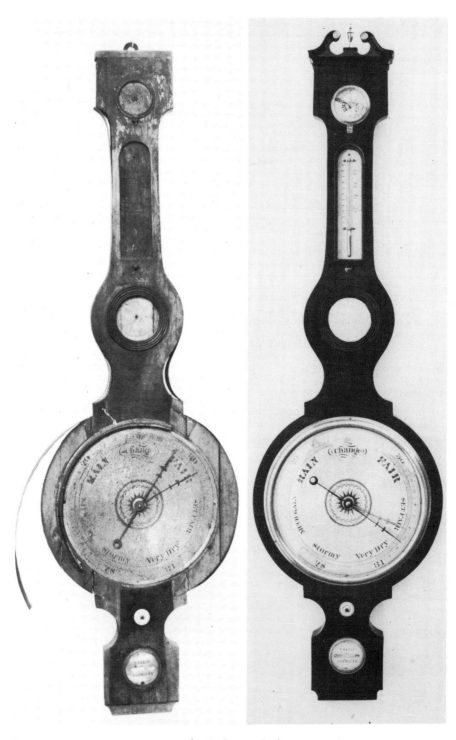

Barometer, c. 1860, before and after restoration.

Preface

This book is aimed to assist the would-be restorer in the finer techniques of barometer restoration in an effort to reduce the number of barometers that are spoiled by poor repairs. I have come across many that have been tinkered with and have had hours wasted on them all because of a lack of knowledge of the finer points of barometer maintenance and repair. In contrast to the devaluing effects of a poor repair, correct restoration will increase the value of a barometer.

In describing the various steps to restore these wonderful instruments correctly, I have assumed the reader to have some previous experience — to be, perhaps, an already fairly competent restorer or at least a practical, do-it-yourself person. Many of the techniques are straightforward, so you should not be frightened of attempting some of the simple work, but, if in doubt or not sure of your own skills, then do not continue work on what is likely to be a valuable instrument — let an expert do the job! We all have different abilities, so don't feel defeated if you have to pass the work on. The end result is what is important.

Chapters 8 and 9 on aneroid barometers and barographs, an increasingly popular section of the barometer market, have been written by Edwin Banfield, barometer collector and author of several books on barometers. I am grateful to him for contributing his expert knowledge of the subject and also for providing over sixty illustrations for the book.

My thanks go also to Joan, whose persistence greatly encouraged me in this work, and to Tom who, although he probably wished that I collected almost anything but barometers, has (so far) constantly come to my aid. Finally, I should like to thank the many friends, colleagues, antique collectors, dealers and enthusiasts who have helped and encouraged me in my barometer mania!

Important Notice

Chemicals are dangerous, and proper care must be taken whenever handling, storing and using all the materials, chemicals, knives and other hazardous items mentioned in this book.

A temporary water wheel barometer constructed by the author against the wall of a church tower. It was approximately 39 ft high and made of plastic tubing formed at the bottom into a large siphon tube with a weight resting on top of the water inside the short limb. As air pressure changes, the level of water moves and this is indicated by a 4½ ft pointer over a 6 ft dial.

Water is, of course, a far less suitable liquid than mercury for measuring atmospheric pressure. It is subject to freezing, expansion and evaporation and so a water wheel barometer requires constant maintenance. Large water barometers were certainly built, but the only working one today, it is believed, is a cistern type made of glass in Bert Bolle's barometer museum in Holland.

1

The Wheel Barometer

A wheel barometer is any type of liquid barometer which transfers the vertical movement of the liquid to an indicating pointer by means of a wheel. This invention is attributed to Robert Hooke around 1664 (*Fig.* 1.1). It is not impossible to use liquids other than mercury, although it is unlikely. Wheel barometers have been successfully demonstrated using water, although the obvious problem here is the height of water needed to obtain sufficient weight to create a vacuum.

The wheel barometers discussed in this book generally have 'banjo'-shaped cases and incorporate a wheel and silk strings holding weights. *Fig.* 1.2 demonstrates the mechanism of a mercury wheel barometer, showing the workings usually hidden within the case. Some of the more common designs of wheel barometer are illustrated in *Figs* 1.3—1.7.

Another type of wheel barometer occasionally encountered has a rack and pinion movement: the wheel is the pinion or cog, and a direct link is made between the float on top of the mercury and the rack (see *Fig.* 3.8). This seems to be found only on Victorian barometers, generally with rounded or 'onion-top' design cases. The dial invariably has the word 'patented' followed by a number, which refers to the patent number for the rack and pinion movement. Either of these types of wheel can be mounted into a case or on a board. They need not always be in a banjo-shaped case. Some of the more rare and usually earlier types of case are shown in *Figs* 1.8—1.11. All of these have wheel movements.

It is a surprising fact that the diameters of the wheels of antique barometers vary considerably in size, differing between 10 mm and 12 mm. As the siphon tube (*Fig.* 1.12) is the standard type of mercury tube used to operate a wheel barometer, the rise or fall of the mercury is the same at A as at B, so whereas, for example, the mercury rises 1 in (that is to say, the distance measured between the level of mercury at the top and that in the lower limb increases by 1 in) the actual rise in the lower limb is only ½ in. Therefore, as most mercurial wheel barometers have a dial which is divided into 3 in over 310°, the wheel needs to be able to move 310° for 1½ in movement of mercury in the lower limb, thus needing to have a 1.741935484 in circumference, which gives a diameter of 0.554475285 in. Some allowance would be needed for the thickness of cord used, but certainly the variations found in old barometers are considerable, only further proving the point that most of these types of instrument were truly 'domestic' and not intended for scientific recording.

Whilst many barometers may be correct, or near, at between 29 in and 30 in, either end of the normal scale (i.e. 28 in and 31 in) will truly show whether these instruments are accurate or not when compared with a scientifically accurate barometer. All this having been said, it is not advisable to alter or change the wheel in a barometer except when missing or badly damaged.

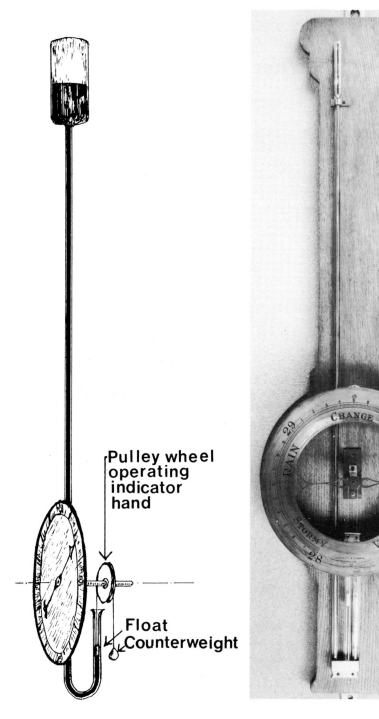

Pulley wheel
operating
indicator
hand

Float
Counterweight

Fig. 1.1 Wheel barometer described by Robert Hooke, c. 1664.

Fig. 1.2 The mechanism of a mercury wheel barometer (*Science Museum, London*).

2

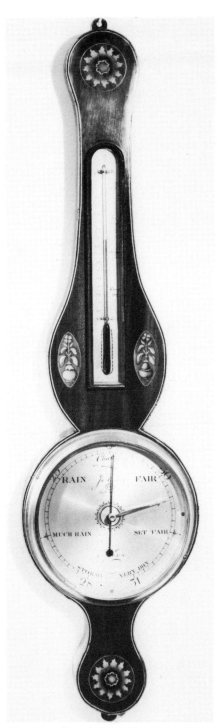
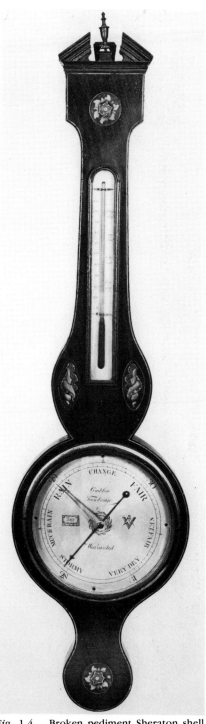

Fig. 1.3   Round top with inlays of floral   *Fig.* 1.4   Broken pediment Sheraton shell
paterae, c. 1790.   barometer, c. 1820.

3

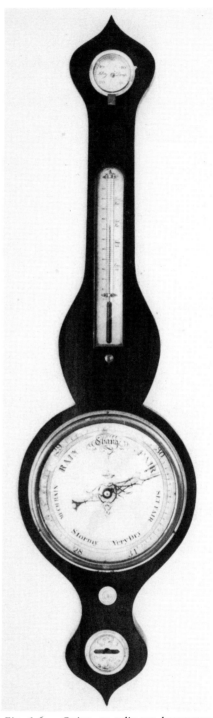

Fig. 1.5 Scroll or swan-neck pediment
barometer, c. 1840.

Fig. 1.6   Onion or tulip-top barometer,
c. 1855.

4

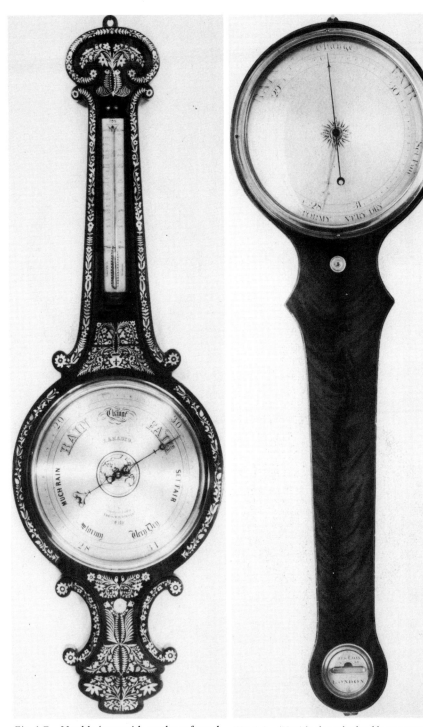

Fig. 1.7   Moulded top with mother-of-pearl inlay, c. 1870.

Fig. 1.8   'Upside down' wheel barometer, c. 1810.

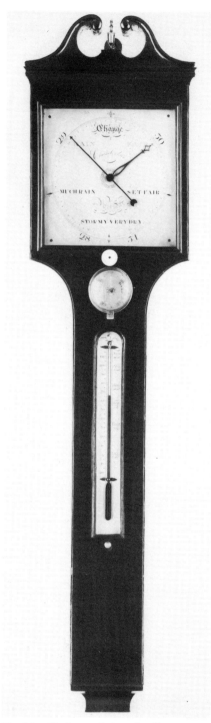

Fig. 1.9 Clock case design wheel barometer, c. 1805.

Fig. 1.10 Barometer incorporating rectangular mirror, c. 1840.

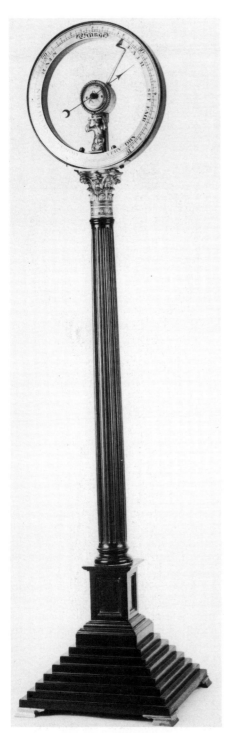

A ⟶ ⟵ Vacuum

⟵ B

Fig. 1.11   Pillar wheel barometer, c. 1850.   *Fig.* 1.12   A siphon tube.

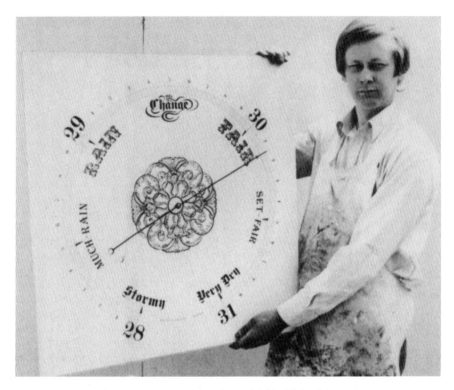

Fig. 1.13   The author with his 26 in dial.

A wheel barometer, by its very design, enables the degree of movement of mercury to be more easily noticed at a glance, and the larger the dial, the greater the enlargement of the movement. *Fig.* 1.13 shows a 26 in dial. If the mercury rises 1 in, the movement is enlarged on this size dial to almost 23 in.

Anyone wishing to try their hand at barometer restoration would do well to start with an onion-top wheel barometer. These can often be bought in a poor state at very reasonable prices, and, if you do not value your time too much, they make good practice pieces, rather than the more expensive ones. The first barometer I restored completely (case and works) was a rosewood onion-top. I bought it for £5 from a dealer who had stripped everything off it (except the door catches and hinges) to put into a door of a grandfather clock! Everything on it now is a replacement, including the thermometer box (*Fig.* 1.6). This is probably why I have a soft spot for the old onion-top barometers, more than most dealers and restorers.

General Care

A phrase to remember when handling mercurial barometers is 'Never lay it flat!' Once hung on the wall, the average wheel barometer should need little maintenance other than an occasional dusting with a soft cloth or the use of a fine brush around the head and mouldings. It is not often necessary to wax polish the case once restored, but a few may require this according to the type of finish or its condition. This can be done by removing the barometer to a safe place where it can lie at an angle of about 40°, then polish carefully.

The brass items on a barometer are traditionally lacquered. If these become tarnished or unsightly they may need to be polished and relacquered but they will need to be removed for this (see chapters 2 and 3). The glasses may need an occasional clean with window polish but only very infrequently, a duster being the most useful item for general maintenance.

It is more useful to look inside the back of the barometer every year or two to see what is happening there. It may be that a spider has crawled in and made a nest, or other insects have found a home. They will probably do no harm, but once a build-up of dust accumulates around the strings and weights and pulley wheel it will probably cause sluggishness of the move-ment, and freedom of the movement in the wheel assembly is paramount for successful operation. After a few years there will also be a build-up of oxides and dust around the bottom of the lower limb of the mercury tube where the mercury rises and falls most often. This can usually be rectified by first trapping the silk strings in position with a piece of card or masking tape, and then removing the heavy weight from the mercury tube, cleaning carefully with tissue and letting it hang down the side. Lastly, clean the in-side of the tube with a pipe cleaner or possibly a feather to remove most of the dirt. This should be all that is needed to maintain your barometer in good working order, but do take care in handling the mercury (see chapter 4).

The hygrometer which is found on some barometers should be checked occasionally. Often the wild oat beard with which it should be fitted has perished and may need replacing at very little cost. Remove the hygrometer and access to the oat beard can usually be found by unscrewing the two halves which make up the assembly. See chapter 3 for replacing the oat beard.

If a barometer fails to sit balanced on the wall fit two small pieces of cork on the back. This will prevent the barometer rocking on the protruding hinges, and will protect your wallpaper. If cork pieces are fitted and the barometer still rocks, continue to balance it by placing more packing on one side or both sides according to the shape of the wall or any warp in the barometer case.

'Should I, or should I not, tap my barometer?' is a question frequently asked. Certainly, a gentle tap should do no damage and will take up the in-evitable slack in the silk threads and thereby indicate the best reading and the direction of the reading. The barometer hand should not move a lot when you tap it. If you find it moves a few inches, this would indicate some dirt or a problem in the mechanism which may require attention.

The best place to hang a barometer is really up to the owner. There is no reason to hang it on an outside wall, outside or even in view of the weather! Air pressure, which is what a barometer measures, is equal in all directions at any given height. As mercury, like all metals, expands in heat, you should not hang the barometer in a position where the room temperature is con-stantly changing. Over a radiator, or other direct heat, is an obvious 'no'. Do not hang it where strong sunlight will fall on it as the sun will invariably fade part of the case; also, the heat generated by sunshine through glass can sometimes be enough to make the veneer lift, as it is normally stuck down with animal glue, and the case may possibly shrink or crack.

The beauty of a domestic barometer is probably more important to the owner than its accurate operation, so hang it where it looks best. It is not a good idea to hang it above a chair in a hallway, for example, as it may easily be knocked. You would be best advised to hang it in a position where you see it regularly. That is why, traditionally, barometers were mostly hung in the hall for gentlemen to regard as they went out, but in today's houses where we often use a side or back door, and rarely open the front door, this is not always the best position. Instead, at the top or bottom of the stairs, provided it will not get knocked, is probably a good place. Outside a bathroom would be fine, or your bedroom, or even the kitchen or breakfast room may prove ideal. By keeping a regular eye on the variations of the air pressure you will be able to make the best use of your barometer. Of course, the practical position and the one that looks the best are not always the same — perhaps a good enough reason to have two barometers!

If there are likely to be marauding children or grandchildren around the barometer, then wire it to the hanging screw through the hanging plate on the barometer when you are putting it in position. This may also deter any potential thief who calls at the door and sees it hanging near the entrance. It is not always possible to use the hanging plate to secure it in this fashion; if this is the case, another hanging plate may be fitted.

Transporting

Great care should be taken whenever moving a wheel barometer. Whilst hanging innocently on a wall no harm will come to the mercury column or tubes, but once moved the mercury is thrown into a paroxysm of oscillations which sometimes causes problems. The first thing to remember is that the level of mercury in the tube will try to maintain its atmospheric height whatever happens to the angle of the tube. Therefore, as you lean the barometer back, the mercury will apparently rise in the tube. At a certain angle the tube will be completely filled and any further angling down of the tube will not cause a change in the level, provided the angle is not so great as to allow the reservoir of mercury in the lower limb to escape. An angle of 25—45° is usually acceptable (*Fig.* 1.14).

If you are taking a barometer from one room to another, then an upright position is fine so long as care is taken, but when carrying a barometer further it should be held at an angle. If transporting the barometer by car, travel with it across the car, i.e. left to right, so as to avoid a possible surge of mercury when braking. Many restorers fit plugs to the tube to prevent spillage of mercury. Tilt the barometer back gently, remove the larger weight, place the plug into the mercury and slide the cork down. Never rely totally on this and always travel with the head of the barometer slightly raised. Better safe than sorry. It is also not a good idea to carry the barometer upright when plugged as the weight of the mercury will always try to force past the plug. For extra security, when moving any mercurial barometer, enclose at least the bottom half of the instrument in a polythene bag (make sure there are no holes in it) to contain any possible spillage of mercury.

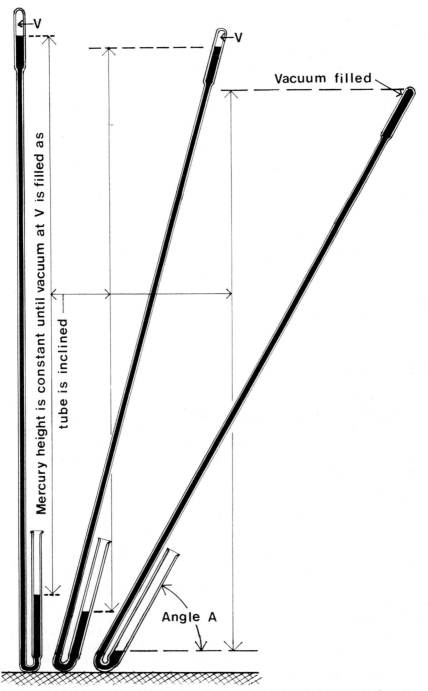

Mercury height is constant until vacuum at V is filled as tube is inclined

Vacuum filled

Angle A

Fig. 1.14 Diagram showing the behaviour of mercury when the tube is lowered. Always carry at an angle less than at 'A', but never flat.

Setting

First find the height above sea level where the barometer is to be placed. Within 50 ft is more than adequate for the usual domestic barometer, and within 200 ft of accuracy is usually satisfactory. In round figures, for every 100 ft above sea level a barometer's reading will be approximately $1/10$ in less than the reading at sea level. Your local Meteorological Office can usually supply the sea level reading for your own area. Radio and television stations occasionally give the pressure in inches or millibars. However, checking against another barometer is probably the quickest and easiest method. An accurate chart showing the various readings can be found in chapter 8.

'Setting' means making the indicating hand read correct and this is most easily done by lowering (to raise the reading) or raising (to lower the reading) the actual mercury tube inside the back of the barometer. When restoring a barometer it is useful to make allowances for this if there is room for movement. If you cannot do this, then it may be necessary to remove the bezel from the front of the barometer, take the hand off carefully and, whilst the barometer is hanging from a central hook (a beam or ceiling), replace the hand in the correct position. Check that the hands are clear of each other and replace the bezel. Constant removal of the bezel will mean loosening of the screws, so do not attempt setting by this method unless you are confident.

Common Faults and Repairs

Many barometers, especially those bought in sales, are in need of some repair. Often the battered-looking barometer can easily be made good, especially if there is a good colour on the case and not too much repair is needed to the woodwork. A good polish can work wonders. Some of the more common faults, which should not deter you from buying a barometer if it otherwise looks in good order, are listed below. More detailed guidance, of course, is given in the following chapters.

Broken Glass

A cracked glass on a thermometer box can often be replaced by oneself, using old glass if you have it, which is thinner and a better colour for old barometers. A collection of old picture glass can be invaluable for this. Thermometer boxes with bowed glass will need making specially, and unless you can make accurate templates, glaziers require the box to fit.

Convex glasses on the dial are usually fitted with plaster of Paris. The old plaster can be cleaned out, the bezel cleaned up, and a new glass from the supplier re-set with plaster of Paris. Make sure most of the plaster is removed and tidy before it sets hard, then use some wire wool to clean away the remainder. When satisfied, lacquer the brass bezel.

Level and hygrometer glasses are traditionally convex and hand-fitted into the bezel. These should be cut and fitted specially but it is possible to find a near size and glue it in position. Your choice will depend on which type of restoration job you require.

Damaged Pediments

These need rebuilding or replacing. Measure the maximum width of the barometer where the head fits, and the depth if large. Heads usually need cutting to depth size, fettling a little and colouring to suit. Missing finials can be replaced with a good style substitute.

Dirty Mercury Tubes

Old mercury tubes need removing, cleaning and topping up, then re-fitting. Broken tubes can rarely, if ever, be repaired satisfactorily.

Corroded Dials

Dirty dials can be cleaned up; corroded dials will need cleaning and re-silvering.

Missing or Wrongly Fitted Parts

These can be corrected or fitted with accurate replacements to maintain a barometer in good condition and value. Many of these are readily available or easy to make. If the hygrometer oat beard is dried up, dropped off or never ever fitted, replace with a new oat beard and dried grass pointer.

2

Dismantling a Wheel Barometer

The first job to do when dismantling a barometer is to remove the glass tube of mercury (or broken pieces). This is easily done by lying the barometer at an angle face down on a table or stand (*Fig.* 2.1; see also Appendix I) and opening the door, thus revealing the tube and rack. Tubes are normally wired into the pine case with two or three wires. Untwist or cut these with a pair of wire snips, bend open the two ends, slide out the glass weights and remove the tube. Remember *not* to lay the tube flat, but keep it at an angle. Next, cut the thread retaining the glass weights on the pulley wheel and remove the glass guide tube. Place the tube of mercury aside *safely*, and place the guide tube and weights in a box.

With the mercury tube removed, the barometer can be laid flat quite safely, although I usually continue to work on the stand — purely out of habit. Now turn the case face up and ease down the clip retaining the hygrometer; lift the bottom of the hygrometer upwards and then pull down (*Fig.* 2.2). Place the hygrometer aside. Unscrew or lift nail and remove the hygrometer retaining clip.

Thermometer

Unscrew the brass knob just below the thermometer box and slide down about $1/8$—$3/16$ in. Hold down, and lift the bottom of the thermometer box up, and then slide down and out (*Fig.* 2.3).

Barometers vary in their style of thermometer box. Generally, Georgian ones are built into the case, so that the bottom piece of moulding needs to be removed by lifting up, or pressing firmly away from the mitres, to gain access to the plate and thermometer tubes (*Fig.* 2.4). About 1820 onwards thermometer boxes were let into the barometer case and retained with a thermometer bolt (as described above). Around 1850, some cheaper barometers were made with the box recessed but glued or tightly fitted with a dummy thermometer bolt, usually just hammered in beneath the thermometer box. Later again, around 1860 onwards, the rectangular form of thermometer box was made, with extra moulding at the top and bottom (see *Fig.* 1.7). This was fitted by use of keyhole slots in the back of the thermometer and retaining screws in the case of the barometer, so that, by sliding the thermometer box up about ⅜ in or ½ in, the thermometer can be lifted straight off (*Fig.* 2.5).

There are, of course, other variations. It is an annoying feature of some later and cheaper barometers that the screws holding the thermometer clips are longer than usual and go through the back and into the barometer case, or the box has been glued in position. It sometimes pays to dismantle the thermometer box *on* the barometer (see below).

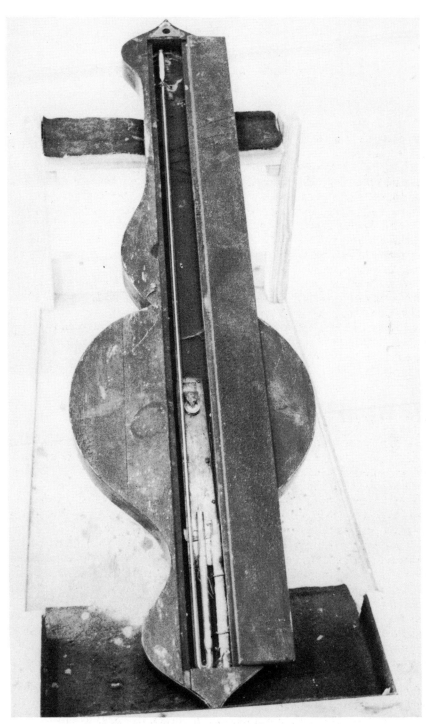

Fig. 2.1   Barometer at an angle on stand.

15

Fig. 2.2   Removing the hygrometer.

Fig. 2.3   Removing the thermometer box.

16

Fig. 2.4 Lifting base moulding from built-in thermometer box.

Fig. 2.5 Fittings of lift-off thermometer box.

17

Mirror

Most mirrors and frames are either a tight fit or are held down with a small amount of glue. Occasionally, you will find that they have been nailed or screwed through the frame, in which case you will need the aid of a screwdriver or pair of wire cutters to remove them. Those that are glued can be removed with careful leverage around the edge of the frame, against the case of the barometer, ensuring adequate protection to the case with packing (*Fig.* 2.6).

When excessive glue has been used by an incompetent restorer, you may have to break the mirror and remove the remaining pieces of glass and cardboard, in order to gain better leverage or to soften the glue with methylated spirits or steam. Be very careful, however, not to damage the veneer of the case.

Level

This, like the mirror frame, is usually just a tight fit, and careful leverage with a strong, thin-bladed knife or similar should result in the ring coming out easily. The level plate is then removed by unscrewing or removing the nails retaining the plate, with small pliers or wire cutters; again, leverage is sometimes useful with the aid of a small, stout screwdriver and a small block of wood against the side of the recess and nail head (*Fig.* 2.7). When loosened, lift out with small pliers.

Dial Bezel

This is normally a simple job of removing the screws or nails which retain the brass ring to the case. Take care to support the bezel and glass when removing the penultimate fixing, as when only one holding screw is left the bezel can slide downwards on that remaining screw and can scratch the dial and case.

Some mid- to late Victorian barometers have cast bezels with flat bevelled glass, and are retained by three bolts passing through the barometer case and held with nuts on the reverse. These bezels are also often let into the case slightly, but removal of the nuts from the thread and just lifting straight upwards will easily remove them.

Finials

These are normally just hammered in on a square tapering shank, sometimes glued. The later styles are screwed in, so try gently pulling off with the fingers, or unscrewing.

Fig. 2.6   Using packing to protect case when lifting mirror frame.

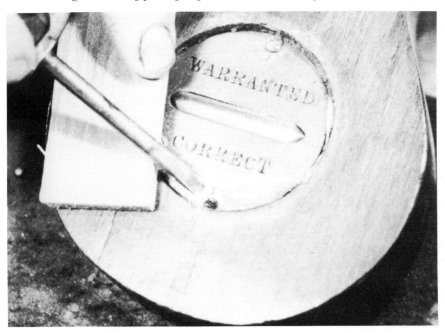

Fig. 2.7   Levering rusted screw from case.

19

Hands

Place one hand (yours) behind the dial and hold the pulley wheel with fingers. With the other hand, hold the long indicator hand in the centre and twist, pulling upwards at the same time, and place aside. The brass recording hand (set hand) will usually pull off with the fingers, but if not, try gentle leverage with a padded screwdriver around the edge of the centre of the hand (*Fig. 2.8*).

Dial

This is normally held by four screws or nails which, when removed, release the dial. If the screws are rusty, apply heat to the head of the screw with a soldering iron for a couple of minutes, and try to undo it with a screwdriver that fits the slots of the screws — filing one to fit, if necessary. If this fails, or the dial is held by nails, use a strong, thin-bladed knife, or similar, to slip under the dial, and slide the edge of the blade close to the fixing nails. With a small amount of leverage the dial usually lifts out the screw. Treat each screw in turn.

Now that all the fittings have been removed from the face of the barometer, all that is left to do is to turn the barometer over on its face side and continue as follows.

Rack and Tube Wires

Unscrew or lift nails and remove the rack. Usually these screws or nails are rusted tightly in, so the use of a long, strong but thin-bladed knife slid under the rack can sometimes lever up those awkward retainers. Heating the screws with a soldering iron often helps. Then remove all remaining old wires, screws and/or nails used to retain the mercury tube and guide tube and, with a sharp knife or chisel, clean away any surplus glue and corks (sometimes used to secure the guide tube).

Thermometer Box

With the thermometer box removed from the barometer, carefully remove the end of the box, the construction of which may vary. On the rectangular box it usually slides upon a small dovetailed tab (*Fig. 2.9*) occasionally screwed, but more often glued in place, and a gentle tap may be necessary. The round-top moulded boxes usually have a fine mortise and tenon joint which is often just a tight fit and should lift straight up (*Fig. 2.10*). If not, then care must be taken not to break it. If the case needs re-polishing, then melting the joint with methylated spirit, or steaming, would probably help. However, if the polish is in good condition, then force may be necessary and a repair probable. Remember, when reassembling this, to use only a small amount of glue so that the next restorer does not have the same problem

Fig. 2.8   Levering set hand from pulley wheel.

Fig. 2.9   Dovetail assembly on lift-off thermometer box.

Fig. 2.10   Removing tenon from mortise.

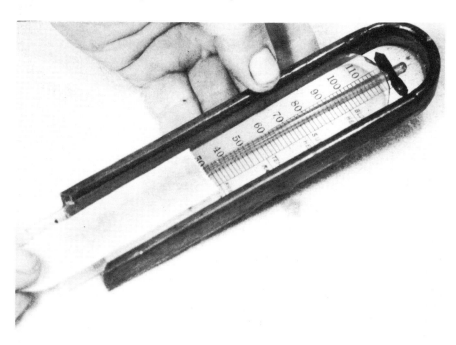

Fig. 2.11   Removing tight glass from groove with masking tape.

22

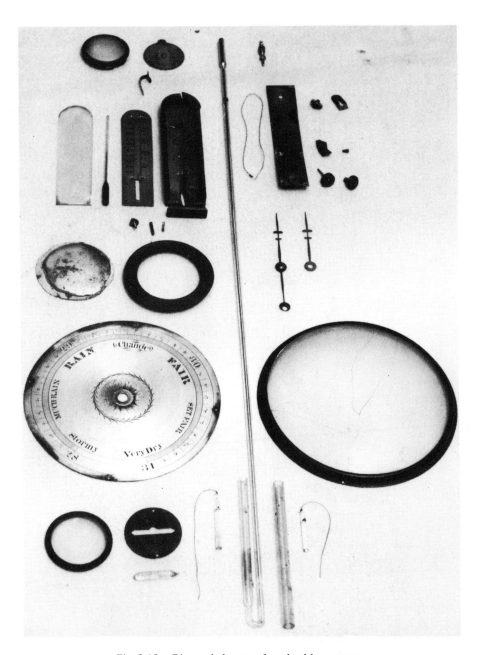

Fig. 2.12   Dismantled parts of a wheel barometer.

23

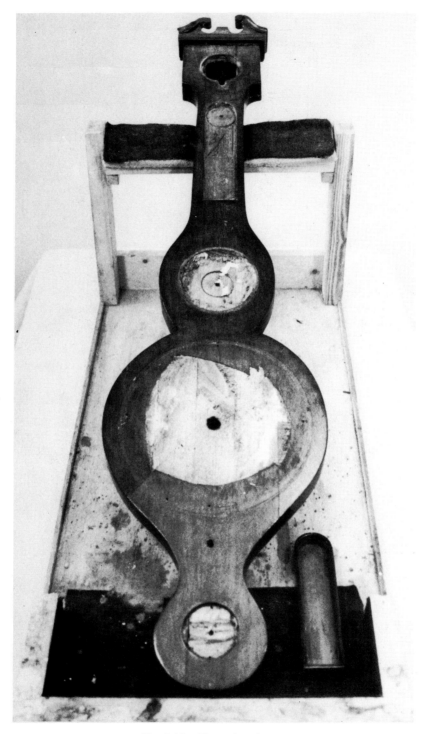

Fig. 2.13   The stripped case.

as you had. The later plain type of thermometer box is usually just a straightforward glued mitre joint. Firm pressure or a slight tap with a block of wood in front of the hammer will shift the joint.

With the retaining piece removed, the glass should slide out. If tight, the use of masking tape (*Fig.* 2.11) can assist in withdrawing the glass from the thermometer box. Remove the screws holding the thermometer tube in position. Brass pins are sometimes used, in which case small pliers will soon extract these quite easily.

Lay the thermometer tube aside carefully — replacement thermometers are difficult to obtain and not usually as good as the original — with clips and screws. Withdraw the engraved thermometer plate which can occasionally be tight, but usually lifts out.

All this completed and you will have a boxful of characteristic looking brass items (*Fig.* 2.12) and a barometer case devoid of much elegance but still with plenty of character (*Fig.* 2.13).

Standard Wheel Barometer Parts

Case
Thermometer box
Thermometer box glass
Thermometer tube
Thermometer plate
Thermometer loops
Thermometer knob
Thermometer bolt
Thermometer spring
Finial
Ivory paterae
Bezel
Bezel glass
Dial indicating hand
Set hand
Set knob
Set knob collet
Level ring
Level ring glass
Level plate
Level bubble
Hygrometer ring
Hygrometer ring glass
Hygrometer plate (dial)
Oat beard

Oat beard pointer
Hygrometer centre (oat beard holder)
Hygrometer centre spring
Hygrometer centre taper pin
Hygrometer clip
Hanging plate
Head
Rack plate
Wheel
Wheel bracket
Set hand pulley
Set knob pulley
Set knob pulley spring
Mercury-filled tube (siphon tube)
Guide tube
Balance weight
Operating weight
Pulley loop
Silk cords
Hinges
Catches
Mirror frame
Mirror
Mirror retaining card
Mirror nails

3

Cleaning and Repair
of Wheel Barometer Parts

Cleaning Fitments

Brass

Once the brass items have been removed, it is best to clean all of them with
the exception of the hinges and the turn catches — when looking at the back
of an antique barometer, it should *look* old! There is also no need to clean
the back of the hygrometer dial, including the taper pin and spring and the
threaded dial holder. It is not advisable to soak the set key as you risk spoil-
ing the bone or ivory, but the spindle can be polished with wire wool —
it generally soon cleans up. As for the rest of the items, soak them in a cleaning solution used by clock-makers. A suitable one can be made up for yourself,
if you wish (see Appendix II) using a large, screw-top jar, or similar, to keep
in the ammonia fumes. Place the items to be cleaned into a solution, including
those with fitted glass, and ensure that they are completely submerged. After
an hour or so, drain off the liquid and wipe off most of the cleansing solution; then fine wire wool and metal polish rubbed over will usually shift
the remaining dirt.

Once cleaned, they can be buffed on an electric polishing pad or left
looking semi-matt and then clear lacquered with two coats of brass lacquer.
Some people prefer slightly coloured lacquer, such as pale gold. It is not
essential to lacquer the brass items but they soon tarnish if not treated, and
polishing the many brass fitments on a barometer is not to be recommended
as it usually leads to unsightly deposits of polish and wearing of the French
polish, causing discoloration. Lacquering the rack is sensible as it helps to
prevent the mercury fumes from discolouring it.

Ivory and Bone

Few of the recommended ways of cleaning ivory seem satisfactory for the
barometer items made of this material. Usually excessive cleaning is not
necessary. Cleaning with fine wire wool to remove surface dirt and grime,
followed by waxing with pure beeswax polish and shining up, will quite often
produce a good patina shine. However, with ivory or bone dials or register
plates, *do not* try cleaning — you will easily rub some of the black engraving into the face of the ivory or bone and spoil the plates. Instead, just a
light wipe over with a slightly dampened cloth will usually take off the surface dirt. Stale bread rubbed over, as in paper cleaning, can also be effective,
but do not rub very hard. Once cleaned, a thin coat of pure beeswax polish,

and then slight buffing by hand with a soft cloth, will often produce a cleaner-looking ivory plate. These are generally only found on stick barometers but sometimes a wheel barometer may have an ivory or bone thermometer plate (probably from another barometer of the time).

Glass

Traditional window polish and wire wool is to be preferred for cleaning the glass items on a barometer. A good rub is necessary when glasses have been polished over, but all comes off in the end! Some old glass always retains a slightly dirty and/or cloudy appearance. This is its very nature; polish off with clean duster or tissues.

Steel

Steel items (not often very many) can be soaked and then buffed up with wire wool, particularly the steel spindle going through the wheel, which needs to run well. The blue indicating hand can be given a coat of blue lacquer if it is in reasonable order, or else it will need cleaning down with fine sandpaper or emery cloth and then re-blueing. This is best done with heat by arranging the hand either in sand or brass filings (see *Fig.* 3.1) and then bringing the whole arrangement to an even temperature until the hand turns to the required colour. Remove and place in fine oil whilst still hot. Practice will of course be needed to produce a satisfactory result. Another way is by the use of chemicals; quite a good compound can usually be obtained from gunsmiths for blueing gun barrels (see Appendix II).

Silvering Dials

Not all dials will require re-silvering. Those in good order may simply need a gentle wipe over with a damp cloth. When dry, apply a fresh coat of colourless brass lacquer to preserve them longer. On slightly dirty dials try cleaning with cream of tartar on a wet cloth; if not successful, try very gently rubbing with metal cleaner on a soft cloth. If all else fails, or you wish for a better finish, then re-silvering is the only course.

Cleanliness is paramount to obtain the best results. After removal of the dials from the case, ensure that they are flat and that burrs from screw holes are removed. Clean off all old silvering with fine wet-and-dry, used wet, with constant clean water. Use of a sink is most helpful here but make sure that you clean down well afterwards, as the silvering powder is poisonous.

Once the dials are clean all over and the brass is shined, dry well and, if any black wax is missing, heat the dial and apply the end of an engraving wax stick (*Fig.* 3.2) to the area needing more. When melted, rub into the engraving, allow to cool and then clean down flat with fine sandpaper. (The use of a breathing mask is recommended, particularly when sanding the brass dry.)

Fig. 3.1 Blueing the indicating hand in sand.

Fig. 3.2 Refilling the engraving with wax.

28

When level, the next stage is to grain the dials. This is done with fine sandpaper. There are two methods: first, straight graining, which is done vertically to the thermometer plate and hygrometer dial and horizontally to the level plate. This is achieved by holding the engraved plate or dial flat down using gloves or clean cloth (no grease or dirt must be allowed to touch the cleaned brass) and carefully sanding the brass in the direction required, changing the position of your hands as you progress across the dial. The second method is done to the main dial. You need to mount this on a face plate of the lathe, or on a motor, so that the lines can be spun in concentric circles in to the middle (*Fig.* 3.3). It is a good idea to twist the dial on the bench holding a piece of glass paper tightly to the middle around the hole, so that the centre ½ in or so does not get missed when mounted on the face plate. Once grained, do not touch the face of the dials with your hands, and keep them clean at all times; using rubber (latex) gloves is very helpful here.

Place the dials face up on a clean piece of formica-covered wood, or similar, approximately 18 in square, and take to the sink. Some people prefer to wet the brass slightly before applying the silvered paste but this is probably optional — try whichever you like. Apply a positive amount of clean silvering paste (see Appendix II) and rub well into the dial until a silver colour is achieved all over. Rinse under running water, do not allow to dry, but sprinkle some cream of tartar over the dial whilst wet, and rub over with a cloth. This will, in effect, polish the silver you have just deposited on the brass; then rinse well and dry quickly using plenty of clean tissues or rags. When dry, warm slightly in front of a fire or over heat and apply two flowing coats of clear brass lacquer (*Fig.* 3.4). There is no need to waste money on a nice new brush (but *never* use an old one!). Instead, tear up a piece of fine cotton cloth to make a disposable lacquer brush. Use a piece of cotton about 4 × 2 in; fold the outside long edges into the middle, fold the newly formed outside edges in again, making a long, thin four-ply piece of material, and fold in half crossways to make a simple pad or brush. When lacquered, put the dials carefully aside to dry for later re-fitting.

Mirrors and Frames

Sometimes the mirrors are broken or very badly marked. Some tarnishing is quite acceptable, particularly on early barometers and especially ones which have a good patina, but some mirrors may need replacing.

Obtain a mirror which will fit nicely within the rebate of the mirror frame and not be too loose. They are usually fixed with three or four pins in the back of the frame (old gramophone needles suit very well here!) over a piece of card cut to fit. Broken mirror frames can sometimes be repaired, but if not a new one will be needed. A size to fit the hole as near as possible (under rather than over) should be bought, or turned on a lathe. I prefer mirror frames with definite beads. The wooden frames are stained black and then polished black before assembly. When assembled with a mirror, they are usually just held into the case with a few small spots of glue and packing, if needed. Some pieces of wood and a couple of clamps may be needed to hold them flat (*Fig.* 3.5). Many rosewood barometers have brass mirror frames; these are sometimes fitted by brass tacks or screws through the face. The mirror is set in the frame with plaster of Paris like the convex glass for the dial bezel.

Fig. 3.3   Spinning the dial.

Fig. 3.4   Applying a flowing coat of lacquer.

Damaged mirrors cannot be repaired successfully, silver paint or paper doing a very poor job. Re-silvering the glass (not the same as re-silvering the brass dials) is usually too expensive and a new mirror is the usual replacement. Remember to blacken the inside of the mirror frame and the cut edge of the mirror to avoid seeing the inside of the frame.

Racks

Fig. 3.6 illustrates the pieces that normally make up a rack assembly with a set key pulley. *Fig.* 3.7 shows a similar type usually found on early Georgian barometers; these have set hands which are controlled by a brass knob fixed through the centre of the glass, making a rack assembly unnecessary. *Fig.* 3.8 indicates a rack and pinion movement as found on a few Victorian barometers, usually of very high quality.

The standard, or large, rack is commonly in need of cleaning, and the face sides exposed to air (and mercury fumes) should be lacquered. It is particularly important that the wheel bearing is at an angle of 90° so that the set key hand pulley will seat on properly and ensure that both the set hand and the indicating hand can travel parallel to the dial face. Careful bending of this bearing spigot can sometimes achieve satisfactory correction; otherwise, some re-rivetting or careful soldering of the spigot will be necessary.

One can usually tell the better-quality barometer by the quality of the rack: the thickness of the brass and the accuracy of manufacture. Make sure also that it is clean inside and out — a buff with some fine wire wool usually makes a good job. When fitting a new pulley string (which is always advisable as an old one will be likely to break much more easily) use some strong, but not too smooth, thick cotton-type thread which will not stretch easily. Tie a neat little knot and trim the ends and then glue, to avoid the knot undoing in the future. Remember to tie a shorter loop than would appear necessary to make sure of a tight fit (*Figs* 3.9, 3.10). Practice will soon enable you to judge how tight. The smaller the knot the better as this knot will travel over the pulley wheels, and a large knot will cause some resistance when turning the set key or, even worse, travel off the pulley wheel and necessitate removal of the tube and rack. This is the reason why the brass set hand should not be turned around fully, but should be moved to left and right, thereby ensuring the knot travels *between* the pulley wheels and not over them.

It is prudent to check the fitting of the set key at this point, since if it does not fit over the square tapered shank very well, a small amount of filing of the shank will be easier now than trying to file the inside of the set key to make it larger. Some set key pulley wheels are located by a slotted keyhole piece which is secured in position by a small steel rivet. When this rivet needs replacing, a small panel pin cut off to the right length will rivet over well and hold all firm.

On the smaller racks (*Fig.* 3.7) cleaning, lacquering and re-fitting will be found to be a much simpler job, usually helped by the thicker and better quality of the parts used by the earlier makers. With the rack and pinion type (see *Fig.* 3.8) a clean and re-fit will be found to be easily undertaken if familiar with the earlier racks described.

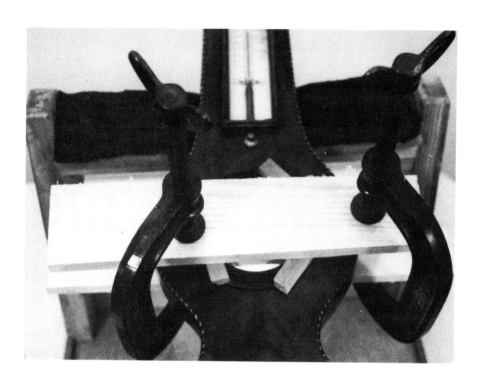

Fig. 3.5   Clamping the mirror frame in place.

Fig. 3.6   The rack assembly parts.

Fig. 3.7   Pulley wheel without set hand mechanism.

Fig. 3.8   Rack and pinion mechanism.

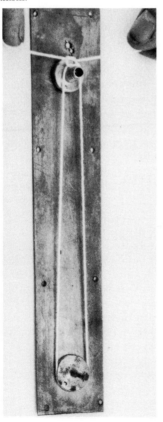

Fig. 3.9   Tying a slightly shorter loop than required.

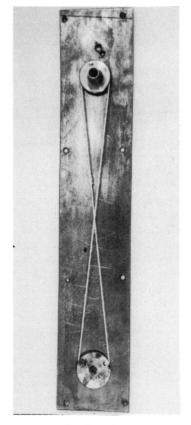

Fig. 3.10   The fitted loop.

33

All these movements should, of course, run dry, but occasionally, on the stubborn sticky one, a small drop of fine clock oil on the bearing will work wonders.

Thermometers

Figs 3.11—3.16 show the more common forms of thermometer found. The early ones were hand-engraved completely but, as time went on, stamps were used for the numbers. This can be clearly seen when comparing thermometer plates. The divisions of some early thermometers can be quite inaccurate to the eye, but this tends to improve as an obvious use is made of a dividing gauge. The thermometer boxes do not vary greatly in design, but rarely will one fit another barometer case. A replacement rounded top can be made by using a lathe to turn up the top piece which is then cut in half (*Fig*. 3.17) and glued to the back board; then fit the side mouldings and, when dry, the end piece.

An unusual but effective little tool can be made to cut the glass groove, by filing the edges of a roofing nail into a saw and holding it in the chuck of an electric drill (*Fig*. 3.18). By holding the moulding fast in a vice, or nailed to the bench if possible, this simple rotary saw will help clean away the waste wood for the groove, provided that deep marking lines have been made where the groove is needed. Of course, this is no substitute for a nice little slitting saw set up on a spindle moulder, but it is far cheaper to make for a single repair.

When ordering a new thermometer plate and tube, make sure that there is sufficient surround to be cut, to enable a good fit of the plate. Three sizes are commonly stocked: 8, 10 and 12 in, each of which will need cutting to fit, drilling for the thermometer loops and silvering. One of the main problems with thermometers is a missing or broken glass tube. These can often be replaced by sending a photostat of the plate to a supplier and describing which type of tube is required, whether the types commonly found on stick barometers (i.e. rounded bulb, clear glass, alcohol-filled) or those commonly found on late Victorian lift-off thermometers (rectangular flat bulb, white-backed glass, mercury-filled).

It is not a serious matter if the column of spirit is broken in a spirit thermometer. Simply hold the thermometer bulb downwards and jolt the wrist against a soft pad — perhaps your other hand or knee — until the spirit reunites. Vigorous action may be necessary, but take care not to strike anything hard. When the main column of spirit is reunited, leave the thermometer standing bulb downwards for several hours to allow the thin film of spirit left on the walls of the tube to drain down to the main column. Always store thermometers upright and away from heat. With mercury-filled thermometers the same procedure is worth trying but does not always work. Instead, a careful application of heat to the bulb will normally reunite divided mercury but practice will be needed: proceed with care.

Hygrometers

These vary little in design until the mid- to late Victorian period when they are found fitted with a false oat beard centre which was never intended to

34

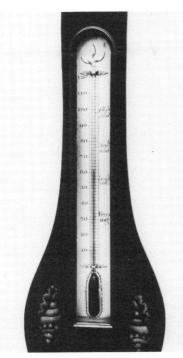

Fig. 3.11   Thermometer, c. 1815.

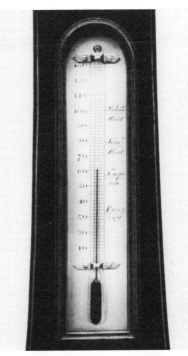

Fig. 3.12   Thermometer, c. 1830.

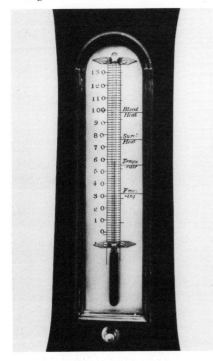

Fig. 3.13   Thermometer, c. 1845.

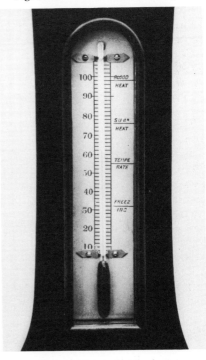

Fig. 3.14   Thermometer, c. 1860.

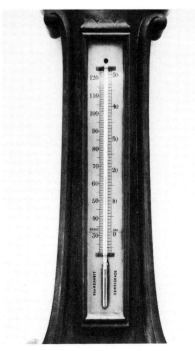

Fig. 3.15 Thermometer, c. 1880.

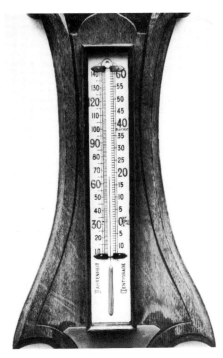

Fig. 3.16 Thermometer, c. 1890.

Fig. 3.17 Turned ring and cut for top of thermometer box.

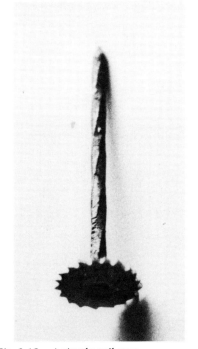

Fig. 3.18 A simple nail saw.

36

work, and at the turn of the century (usually) one can find examples of solid one-piece hygrometer bezels creeping into manufacture, a common feature of today's hygrometers due to cost (*Fig.* 3.19).

The oat beard hygrometer is a rough indicator of moisture in the atmosphere; some are found with badly fitting plates or with pieces cut out of the plates to allow air movement and thereby a quicker response. Moisture levels in domestic houses vary little, other than from summer to winter.

To replace the oat beard (available from suppliers), first unscrew the back plate and ring, clean away the dirty centre, and then pick out a nice oat beard (*Fig.* 3.20). Choose a black, strong-looking fibre. Cut a small piece of dried grass to a length just over the diameter of the plate and make a small knife hole in the centre, then pass one end of the oat beard carefully through this hole and try it in the centre for length. Trim to near size, place a small drop of glue at the bottom of the hole using a fine point, and another droplet of glue on the dried grass pointer where the oat beard emerges. Place the oat beard and pointer in position and make sure that enough glue is in position to hold the oat beard — but *not* too much so as to glue the oat beard solid! Set the assembly aside to dry in a place which is level and the grass pointer is free to turn as the oat beard absorbs the moisture of the glue, and then dries again.

When fitting new hygrometer centres, cut away a section of the stem and file smooth. This allows the air to reach the oat beard quicker and makes for a much better replacement. Some old hygrometers have centres which are cut or filed in a 'V' shape, but either (or neither) will depend on your choice, more than any particular right 'style'. When dried fully, carefully cut the grass pointer (*Fig.* 3.21) so that one end becomes the pointer and the other end balances it. Sometimes a drop of glue can be placed on the shorter end, to try to balance this 'hand' further to help it turn in parallel with the plate. *Fig.* 3.22 shows a complete hygrometer fitted.

Level Ring

There are only two common level bezels: the circular (*Fig.* 3.23) and the oblong frame (*Fig.* 3.24). *Fig.* 3.25 shows the pieces. Both types are held in the case by a tight fit and perhaps a spot of glue to locate. Occasionally, it will be necessary to pack out the recess in the case slightly with cardboard or veneer (coloured, so as not to show) to enable a truly tight fit. The level ring should always match the design of the hygrometer ring and if different, a replacement should be suspected.

Before fitting the level ring or frame, fit the level bubble and level plate. Commonly, the level bubble is seated first on a piece of paper to enable clear reading of the bubble and to cover up the pine which has been exposed; then the level plate is placed on the bubble. It should fit nicely and not allow the bubble through the cut-out section. Although similar to a spirit level at first glance, a barometer level is not in fact the same. On a spirit level the bubble is slightly curved, enabling a slow movement of the bubble to indicate the level. On barometer levels, the bubble is made of straight glass and, when fitted, the very slightest movement will send the bubble racing to one end or the other of its glass.

Fig. 3.19   A complete hygrometer.

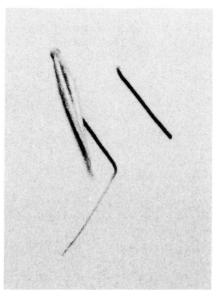

Fig. 3.20   A wild oat seed and a beard removed.

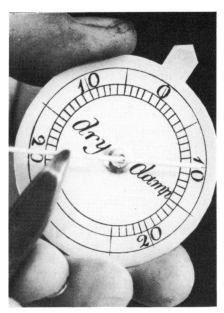

Fig. 3.21   Trimming the pointer.

Fig. 3.22   The complete hygrometer fitted.

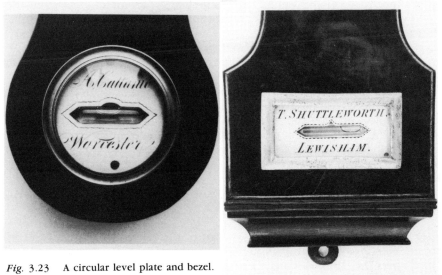

Fig. 3.23   A circular level plate and bezel.

Fig. 3.24   A rectangular level plate and bezel.

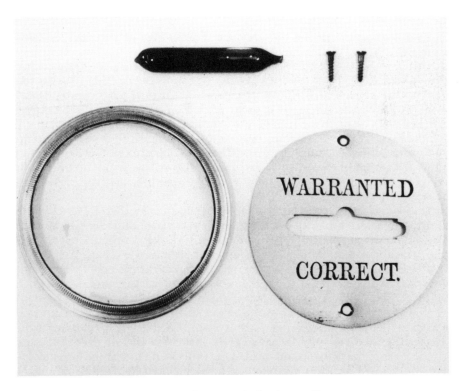

Fig. 3.25   The parts of a level assembly.

Attempt to level the bubble by hanging the barometer case from the ceiling of your workshop, thus ensuring it will be hanging quite upright, and then proceed to fix the level plate so as to hold the bubble centrally. As there is no adjustment other than the screws retaining the plate, it is close to impossible, for even as the screws are tightening, the bubble will begin to move.

Occasionally, the level plate on a barometer will reveal another maker's name and address on the reverse. Perhaps one maker obtained the barometer second-hand, and then had his name and town engraved on the reverse. Alternatively, the engraver may have in error, or by bad debt or disagreement, engraved too many plates for one firm and simply turned them over when needing to supply another firm. The first theory is probably the most likely.

Bezels

Figs 3.26—3.29 show the cross-sections of the commoner types of bezel found on barometers. Although there are some variations in moulding shapes, these cover the major designs. The bezels on Sheraton shell barometers have flat glasses fitted with plaster of Paris, a hole in the centre where the set hand knob enters and the brass hand fixed onto the threaded part by a small brass nut. A small leather or paper washer is used to prevent the glass breaking when tightening the fixing and ensuring free but firm movement of the set hand.

To drill the hole in the flat glass use a glass drill or tile drill available from DIY shops. Always check first the position of the hand in relation to the black indicating hand. Use turpentine or white spirit to lubricate and slowly start to drill in the centre. Plenty of care is needed not to press too hard on the glass while drilling. After a while turn the glass over and start from the other side. The glass must be resting on a flat, clean surface. Once the two holes begin to meet and create a hole right through the glass, slowly file the hole larger with a round needle file, taking care not to jam it tight and possibly risk cracking the glass. The hole needs to be large enough to allow the set knob to sit flat on the glass and turn inside the hole without much sideways movement; remember to clean and lacquer the brass hand before final assembly.

The convex glass style bezel varies more in quality than in actual basic design. Some have plenty of rebate to fit the glass, others only the bare minimum. When fixing a new or old glass in position mix plaster of Paris into a cream and apply a generous amount around the rebate (*Fig.* 3.30). Push the convex glass into position, ensuring that it rests equally and right into the rebate (*Fig.* 3.31), applying more plaster of Paris around the edge of the glass to hold firm when dry. As the plaster of Paris begins to harden, clean away the surplus quickly and try to finish the remainder before the plaster of Paris is hard. Sometimes a Stanley knife will trim away half-hardened plaster. As with flat glass bezels, make sure that no plaster of Paris is visible from the outside and none is beyond the height of the bezel to encumber fitting the back of the bezel to the barometer (*Fig.* 3.32). Some staining of the new plaster may be preferred after cleaning the bezel and glass.

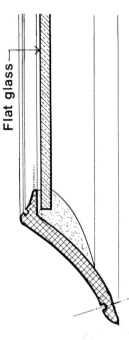

Flat glass

Fig. 3.27   Flat glass Sheraton shell style bezel.

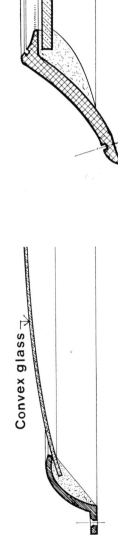

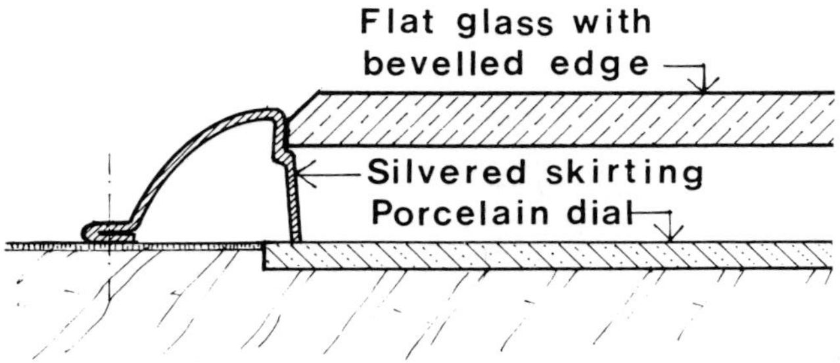

Convex glass

Fig. 3.26   Convex glass style cast bezel.

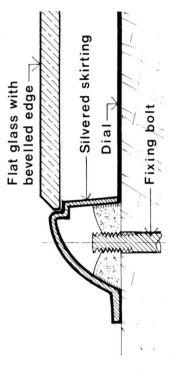

Flat glass with bevelled edge

Silvered skirting

Dial

Fixing bolt

Fig. 3.29   Victorian cast and bolted bezel with bevelled glass.

Flat glass with bevelled edge

Silvered skirting

Porcelain dial

Fig. 3.28   Aneroid barometer bezel with flat bevelled glass.

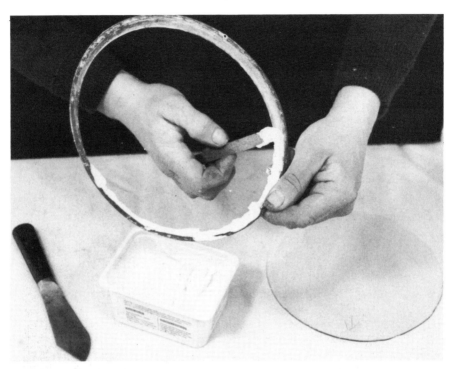

Fig. 3.30   Applying plaster of Paris to inside of rebate.

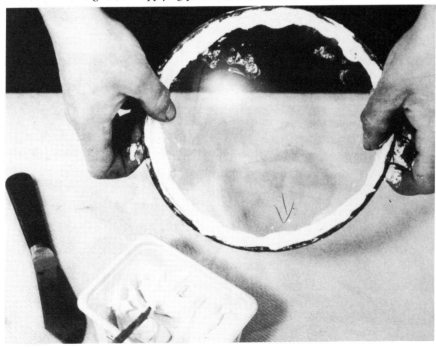

Fig. 3.31   Setting the glass well into the bezel.

42

Fig. 3.32   The fitted convex glass.

Bevelled glass bezels are found on late Victorian barometers, often with rounded heads. If the glass is broken, it will need a new piece making and fitting specially into it. There is a silvered reflecting ring on these types and this should be cleaned and re-silvered if necessary and then lacquered to protect it from corrosion. A new glass will need to be fitted and you should send the bezel to a glass beveller. The glass on this style of bezel is often very thick.

4

Mercury Tubes

Mercury is a hazardous material and, before handling it, suitable precautions should always be taken. Anyone handling mercury would be well advised to read the Guidance Notes issued by the Health and Safety Executive: *Mercury — health and safety precautions* (Guidance Note EH17, HMSO, 1977) and *Mercury — medical surveillance* (Guidance Note MS12, HMSO, 1979). These are available from government bookshops and their agents.

Never work with mercury on the kitchen table or sink but preferably use a special bench (see Appendix I). If you do not intend to use mercury very much, a more temporary wooden bench can be used. Remember, mercury contaminates and should be kept away from all other work. Personal hygiene is paramount. Always use gloves; thin latex gloves are easily available and do not impair handling of these delicate tubes. It is a good idea to have a spare pair ready in case you rip the ones you are using. A separate overall and shoes are also very good practice. A well-ventilated room, or even outdoors in good weather, is ideal; if possible, use a localized extraction unit to carry away the fumes. Remember also that mercury evaporates at room temperature and the warmer it is the greater the rate of evaporation. Do not therefore work with mercury close to any heat. If you have worked, or intend to work, with mercury for some time it is sensible to arrange a urine mercury level test with your doctor.

Once removed from the case, the mercury tube must be kept at an angle, for once laid flat some of the mercury will spill out from the short limb. Nearly all siphon tubes will have collected some dirt from the glass, the atmosphere or simply from some dust entering the case. Occasionally, it will only be necessary to empty the lower part of the tube but more often than not a better job will be made if you empty the tube completely and refill with clean, triply distilled mercury.

Empty the mercury and dust from the container's short end (*Fig.* 4.1), shake and tap the tube until the mercury falls around the bend, and continue this until the tube is quite empty. The use of a clean feather stripped except for the first 2 in and mounted in a rubber tube (such as an old electric cable) (*Fig.* 4.2) will enable cleaning around the bend, and some wire wool, cottonwool or tissue can be worked inside the short limb until perfectly clean (*Fig.* 4.3).

If the inside of the tube is dirty then it is possible to pour about 2 in of nitric acid into the short limb — *take great care*. Cork the top and slowly work the acid around the bend and up the tube. Swirl it around a few times and you will normally find that the dirt is removed. Then, with plenty of water, empty away the nitric acid from inside the tube as well as possible. It will be necessary to pass a small catheter tube inside the mercury tube now (*Fig.* 4.4). Rinse well with clean water, preferably distilled, by connecting the catheter tube to a clean syringe filled with the water and forcing

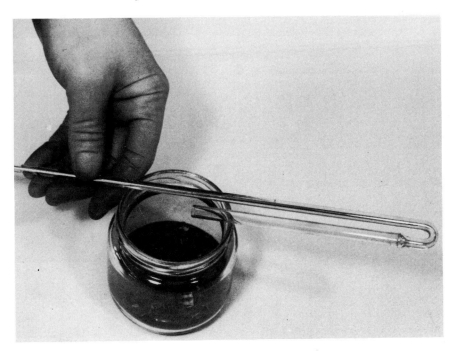

Fig. 4.1   Emptying mercury from the short limb.

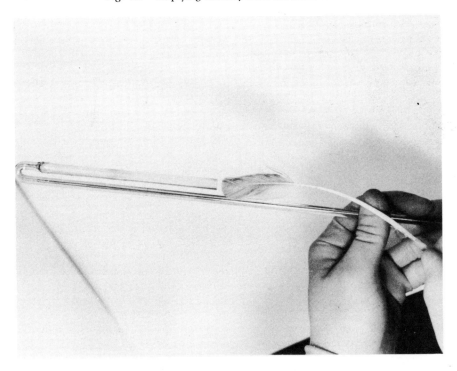

Fig. 4.2   Using a feather to clean round the bend of the tube.

45

Fig. 4.3   Using wire wool to clean the short arm.

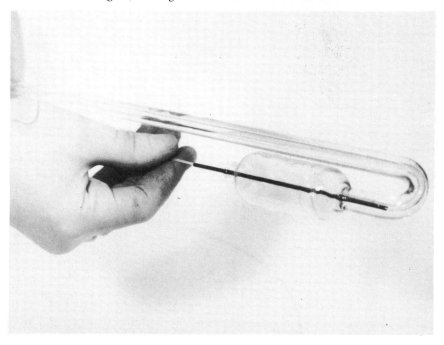

Fig. 4.4   Passing catheter tube up the long arm with the help of a stiffer tube.

it round the tube several times. When all traces of acid are well and truly removed, empty the tube of water as well as possible. Then rinse with isopropylalcohol to remove any traces of water.

Finally, to dry, blow warm dry air into the tube with the aid of a catheter tube connected to a small pump. The air being forced into the tube will push the heavy, alcohol-laden air out of the open end. After a few minutes the tube should be quite dry.

The use of clean catheter tubes at different stages is advisable. Of course, if the mercury glass tube is in a reasonable state the need to clean will not arise. Also, the cost of a new tube will be cheaper and possibly better than cleaning most old tubes, but this cleaning process is of particular value on larger tubes or special tubes which are not easy to replace.

Cleaning the Mercury

To clean mercury, first separate the bulk of the dirt from the mercury by sucking the mercury up a syringe from the centre of a quantity of mercury, leaving the dirt floating on the top and clinging to the sides of the container. Do not try to suck up every drop of mercury as you will undoubtedly pick up some of the dirt. Next, place some of the mercury into a clean cloth or leather and wrap around the edges of the cloth to enclose the mercury, twist and squeeze the cloth until the mercury emerges as fine droplets showering down into a clean container (*Fig. 4.5*).

Another method is to pack a syringe with some cloth and/or tissue to form a filter and top up with mercury. Place the plunger into the top and squeeze the mercury through the filter into a clean container (*Fig. 4.6*).

Once cleaned, the mercury should be suitable to use again in most instances particularly topping up, although it is rarely so good as using triply distilled mercury.

Refilling the Mercury Tube

This has been made easy today with the use of a catheter tube (available from suppliers). Feed up the short limb until it reaches the top. Support the tube upside down at an angle. Connect a syringe with clean mercury in, slowly push the mercury into the catheter tube until it begins filling the glass tube. Slowly remove the catheter as you fill the glass tube. When reaching the bend, carefully lower the tube, squeeze a little more mercury in around the bend whilst raising the top end of the tube.

Fill the short limb only about ½ in, then withdraw the catheter from the mercury and lift the plunger to bring the mercury back into the syringe (some practice will soon make this procedure seem very easy). Place the syringe aside. Lifting the mercury tube upright, the mercury level should fall in the top and rise in the short limb. When leaning the tube back at an angle, an audible 'tick' should be heard. If air is trapped up at the top then no noise will be heard or the tick will be very faint. By corking the open end well you may invert the tube and carefully tap and shake the bubble until it rises to the bend, then gently work it around the bend. By standing the tube

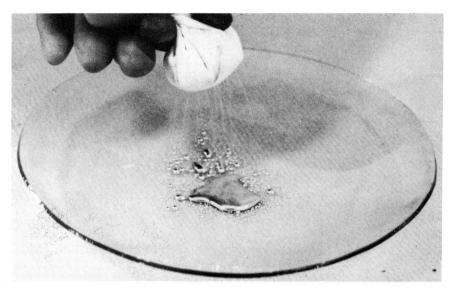

Fig. 4.5   Squeezing mercury through a fine cloth.

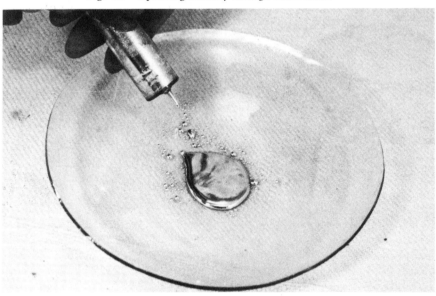

Fig. 4.6   Forcing mercury through a filtered syringe.

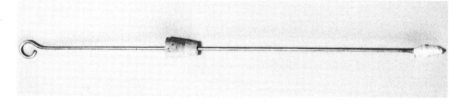

Fig. 4.7   A stainless steel plug.

48

upright, the surge of the mercury usually pushes the bubble of air out into the shorter limb and away. You will probably see small silver dots along the tube; these are air and/or water vapour caught between the mercury and the glass. In old glass tubes the mercury etches away the glass thereby making the inside of the tube slightly rough. This causes bubbles to stick to the sides rather than float upwards. It is always easier to remove the larger bubbles from a new glass tube. In time, these small bubbles will probably find their way up to the vacuum and thereby impair the accuracy of the reading, but with domestic barometers this is usually of little relevance to the readings obtained. In the past, the mercury was boiled inside the tube to assist the removal of bubbles, but this is not to be recommended today due to the *very dangerous* vapour created.

Once cleaned and refilled, make a plug to fit the tube using a cork and stainless steel wire sharpened at one end and wrapped in cotton thread to a taper and then glued (*Fig.* 4.7). This will trap the mercury in the glass tube when transporting the mercury tube or barometer.

5

Case Repairs and Refinishing

The repairs needed to a barometer case can vary tremendously, and while most of us would like to buy a barometer with all its fittings and case perfect (perhaps only needing cleaning) this seldom happens. One can, of course, buy a badly damaged barometer for a very reasonable price, and then have the pleasure of restoring it and finish up with an elegant barometer for a fraction of the cost of buying one in original condition.

In this chapter I shall describe repairs to the cases of barometers in fairly general terms, assuming that the reader has a basic knowledge of tools and terminology; if not, then repairs other than the very simplest should not be attempted.

Woodworm

Woodworm commonly eat into the white/yellow stringing and the pine case of barometers. After the case has been stripped of fitments apply a generous coating of woodworm fluid. Rentokil is probably the best. If the woodworm are active I like to kill them by wrapping the barometer in a plastic bag, sucking the air out (using a vacuum pump) and thereby reducing the amount of water vapour that will freeze and condense when defrosting. Then I seal the bag well with tape and place in the deep freeze, putting it on super freeze. I have not known a woodworm to survive this treatment! After 24 hours remove and carefully defrost, allowing several hours for it to thaw out. For the first half an hour to one hour keep a constant eye on the case and wipe off the condensation which forms because of the temperature variation. Water can damage the polish so I prefer to use this treatment only for barometers which need to be re-polished anyway, in case it spoils the polish. No assurance can be given that the case will not warp or crack but the ones I have treated this way have fared well so far. If using the deep-freeze method, do not treat with woodworm fluid beforehand as this may taint your food; instead, treat after defrosting. This will poison the wood so that you should not suffer any further woodworm infestation in the barometer. After treatment, if necessary, you will need to fill in any holes showing on the polished side. This can best be done with wax stoppers (available from polish suppliers) heated and melted into each hole. If re-polishing, a harder stopper could and should be used. For the back of the case, use a hard stopper such as Timberfill or plaster of Paris rubbed down.

The backs of barometers are usually painted with a Venetian Red wash or similar. These earth powders can normally be bought from polish suppliers. Mix with some glue and water and paint over the back. It should be possible to match the colour by mixing the powder and you will not need to paint the entire back if a suitable match is made. Use this paint mix also if you have to fill in other holes on the back or even put a new door to the barometer.

Head Repairs

Figs 5.1—5.10 give a selection of common styles of barometer head. The two types most frequently in need of repair are the 'broken' (*Fig.* 5.2) and 'swan-neck' (*Fig.* 5.3) pediments. The normal damage to a broken pediment is missing mouldings. As these vary slightly, it is often best to make a moulding tool for each type of moulding as required, or glue a piece of wood in position and shape when dry, using suitable chisels. Small chips can be made good by splicing-in where necessary. A good stock of old mahogany will, of course, come in very handy in matching grain types. A simple cutter (*Fig.* 5.11) can be made and used to make complete heads, or kept in case the same moulding is needed again.

With the swan-neck pediment the usual damage is a broken swan-neck! These can be time-consuming and fiddly to repair, as one has to glue small pieces of wood together, having carefully cut out the correct shape whilst the head is on the barometer. When doing this or re-glueing broken pieces, it is stronger if a small wooden pin is used to help keep the repair in position for years to come (*Fig.* 5.12). It is sometimes better to replace the front part of the head with a new pediment. Old veneered pine is useful here, and make sure that the curves are flowing nicely; in addition, of course, the shaped scroll pieces strengthen the head and sometimes cover a repair (*Fig.* 5.13).

Missing moulding on swan-necks can be replaced as described for broken pediments. Sometimes the centre of both types of pediment is damaged, thereby needing careful paring straight, and glueing suitable veneered timber in place before cutting with a fine fret saw, to shape the inside edges of curves, which were rarely smooth, but just neatly cut in the original. The front scroll pieces are best shaped to fit the first profile and then glued in position and cut to the shape of the head, and then carefully carved with a small gouge (*Fig.* 5.14). If ebony is not available, then an alternative tight-grained timber will serve and can be polished black later. Do not forget the small $3/32$ in platform for the finial to rest on. This just puts the finishing touch to the heads.

Paterae and Inlays

These sometimes become loose but one can usually inject or work glue under the inlay, and clamp down with the aid of some thick Perspex (*Fig.* 5.15). This ensures a flat surface, and the ability to see the work underneath is a great advantage. Using wax on the Perspex will normally prevent it sticking to the inlay. This simple process is also very useful when placing a small piece of veneer in position, as with normal clamps and blocks you cannot see if the piece has slid with clamping, but the Perspex enables you to see over most of the joint and adjust if necessary. When removing, do not lift straight up, but slightly twist first to break any Perspex join with the veneer.

Replacing missing parts of the inlay can be done by placing a piece of paper over the missing shape and rubbing with a candle or crayon, then sticking the piece of paper on to a matching veneer and cutting with a fine piercing saw. Another way is to use some very thin rigid plastic (which you often

51

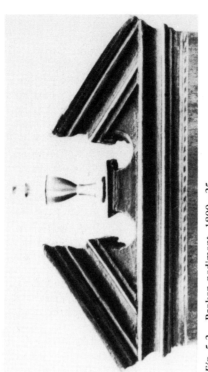

Fig. 5.2   Broken pediment, 1800—25.

Fig. 5.4   Onion or tulip-top, 1850—60.

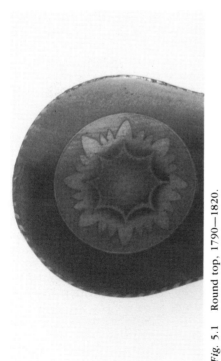

Fig. 5.1   Round top, 1790—1820.

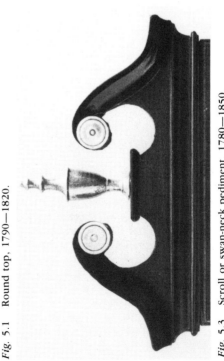

Fig. 5.3   Scroll or swan-neck pediment, 1780—1850.

52

Fig. 5.6   Architectural pediment, c. 1860.

Fig. 5.8   Carved pediment, c. 1870.

Fig. 5.5   Onion-top with scrolls, 1855—60.

Fig. 5.7   Carved pediment, c. 1860.

53

Fig. 5.10 Mother-of-pearl inlay, c. 1870.

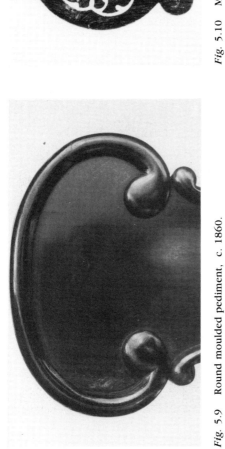

Fig. 5.9 Round moulded pediment, c. 1860.

Fig. 5.11 Double-handled scratch stock mounted with moulding cutter.

Damage
to scroll
repaired
using
dowel

break

Fig. 5.12   Repair using dowel pin behind scroll front.

Fig. 5.13   New scroll section ready to glue to new pediment.

Fig. 5.14   Carving the scroll in position.

find as lids of gift containers) which can be held over missing pieces of inlay with tape. Then, with a fine needle, make a series of dots into the plastic around the shape, before transferring to wood by the use of carbon paper (*Fig.* 5.16).

If inlays are missing or irreparable, then new ones can be made by sandwiching the necessary pieces (i.e. by colourings) between paper and glue and, when dry, marking patterns on top and then cutting through all three at once. A very fine drill will be needed to start some of the cuts, and the essential secret is in a very fine blade and keeping the blade upright, as a slight angle increases the gap when assembling.

After cutting, soak well in hot water and collect the pieces required, glueing them flat to a piece of newspaper. When finally glueing into position, the use of Perspex will again be helpful. Some inlays are shaded, and this is done with very hot sand. With experience, a reasonable job can be made, but often good replacement inlays will be better.

Veneers

Damaged or unsightly veneers around the edges of barometers are the most common faults — mainly lifting and bubbling. If bubbles are not too unsightly you would do best to leave them, particularly if the polish has a good colour; but, when necessary, they will need cutting and glueing — never a totally satisfactory repair — replacement of pieces being a much better solution. You must choose which is best for the type of barometer and its grain.

Broken or missing veneer can be best repaired by scarfing-in matching grained veneer, which is usually straight on the side of barometers. Remember to make as strong a job as possible as, once cut, the length of the veneer always has a tendency to move at a joint. Curved cauls made for this job, and padded with cloth, will help with cramping, and some 12 in or 18 in sash cramps are more easy to use than normal larger ones (*Fig.* 5.17). Masking tape will be very useful here, as indeed it is with stringing repairs. Repairs to cases often mean glueing one or two parts, then leaving them to dry fully, which can sometimes take several days.

Stringing

Many barometers have white and then black stringing around the edges. The white, which is thought to be boxwood, often gets eaten by woodworm, leaving the black line intact. The black (more often than not) is stained fruit wood, and I suspect that the white is sometimes unstained fruit wood, light, straight-grained, no knots and very pliable (to go round curves). With a thin chisel it is possible to pare away eaten inlay and replace with new, leaving this proud and cutting carefully down when the glue has dried.

When the black as well as the white has to be replaced, replace the two together, the one aiding the other in bending and holding. Make sure that the white stringing you are using is the same width as the old. The black can be (and it actually helps if it is) larger in dimension. On longish strips of say 6 in and more, cut the first two as shown (*Fig.* 5.18) and then bend around the new bits slowly, using masking tape and glueing as you go. When

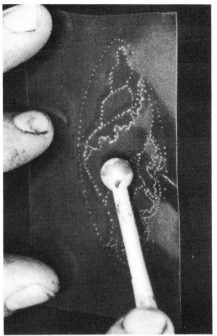

Fig. 5.15   Perspex used to clamp veneer repairs.

Fig. 5.16   Transferring a pattern on to paper using carbon paper.

Fig. 5.17   Sash cramps and shaped cauls holding veneer whilst drying.

near the end, support a block of wood under the new stringing, and carefully cut the end to fit first the white and then the black (which it is useful to make longer anyway). Once dried, they can be pared away carefully with a very sharp chisel, followed by some fine sandpaper (240 grit), keeping away from the good polish, if there is any.

Around acute bends, a softening of the stringing in boiling water will really help prevent breaking and, when dried, will be better resigned to stay shaped. Wrapping pieces in a wet cloth and applying a hot iron on top with reasonable pressure will usually do but, on longer or complete re-stringing jobs, the use of a saucepan or other container of boiling water is necessary.

Applied Moulding

Applied moulding, normally found on late Victorian barometers, is sometimes missing, and here it needs making first. Before glueing in position, shape the inside of the curves, and the outside edges can be trimmed and sanded smooth when fixed.

Where actual decorative carving is missing from the case, this needs re-making. Copy either from the other side (if it is a left and right-sided style carving) or from photographs or drawings of similar carving to make a suitable replacement.

Thermometer Boxes

These sometimes need re-making completely. More commonly the bottom part is missing and a simple repair can usually be effected. Some standard shapes are illustrated in *Figs* 3.11—3.16.

Refinishing the Case

Once the case has been restored satisfactorily, the next task is to bring back a good finish. The type of refinishing will, of course, depend on the finish required. Barometers were often polished with a high shine, particularly the better-quality veneered ones, but people vary greatly in their taste. I seldom like a shiny finish but here are some of the possible ways of finishing a case. I do not intend to deal in detail with French polishing. There are adequate books on the subject that you can consult as necessary.

A small repair to a case will need staining to match, and then a few coats of polish (rubbing down with wire wool between), usually followed by a French polishing rubber and then Brasso to smooth, blend in and shine. Allow sufficient time for the polish to dry. Garnet or Button polish is to be recommended for most polishing jobs, available from polish suppliers.

Where very few or no repairs have been necessary, the finish will depend on how dirty the case is. If it is heavily covered in smoke and grime, or perhaps black varnish (used to freshen up furniture when spring cleaning!), then carefully rub down with a reviver. Harrells Reviver is a good one, but a suitable reviver can be made for yourself (see Appendix II).

If this fails to clean off the dirtier cases then methylated spirit or stripper is needed, in which event, keep at it slowly without rubbing too hard. Try to leave some dark areas in the corners or else the case will look brand new (this is not always possible).

On a fairly clean or lightly soiled case, a metal polish such as Brasso is helpful, used carefully with 0000 wire wool on the stubborn areas, but normally with just a cloth. Once polished with this and then dried, a good dark wax, rubbed in to the case with an old toothbrush and just shone off, is usually the best treatment.

The use of linseed oil or similar is not advisable as it invariably leaves a sticky mess, although if there is damp or water damage to the finish some camphorated oil mixed 50/50 with pure turpentine well rubbed in sometimes helps recover a good colour. When dry, still wax over with a good wax.

You may find that a previous owner or restorer has (for no good reason) put a coat of polish onto the barometer, well after it was new, without (luckily) cleaning down the previous surface — you can often see polish on the bezels as well! These cases appear covered in scratches, but on closer inspection you can, if lucky, scratch off this thin coat of polish with your finger nail (hard-going and time-consuming) to reveal underneath a barometer which has a perfectly good polish and only needs perhaps a clean with Brasso and a good waxing. More often than not, the polish comes off in the obvious places, but begins to be difficult to remove from other areas.

If you suspect that the barometer has a 'second' coat like this, and you decide to leave it as it is in reasonably good order, do *not* place it in the freezer to kill woodworm (see above) as the extreme change in temperature can easily start to lift this second coat (which is not properly keyed into the original) and defrosting it may well start it peeling and blistering, necessitating more work.

Any cases which are beyond the treatment so far described will require *careful* application of methylated spirit to melt away the old polish and try to rediscover a finish underneath. However, as methylated spirit melts shellac polish, this is very tricky to use, and you cannot afford to leave the meths on for a second too long — using wire wool and a cloth to rub the old finish off is the best way. By doing this, you can partly control the rate at which you strip and, therefore, not completely remove all the filler and polish from the grain whilst retaining a good colour; once achieved, put furniture polish over the cleaned case and refinish as usual.

If all else fails, then it is down to the paint stripping and complete removal of finish to enable a fresh start to be made, followed by staining, filling grain, French polishing and so on.

Some of the early barometers do not look attractive with French polish, particulary country stick barometers or Sheraton shell wheel barometers. With these types it is sometimes possible to stain and then wax polish; that is, to put a coat of beeswax polish on the barometer and allow to dry, then polish off with a suitable soft cloth, repeating this exercise as many times as necessary to get an old appearance and nice lustre shine. This type of finish will want working at — possibly every six months — for a few years until a really good depth of finish is achieved. Therefore, it is not always suitable for barometers you may wish to sell, or for those belonging to customers who will not want to polish them.

Fig. 5.18   Stagger and angle stringing repairs.   *Fig.* 5.19   An old cast hinge.

A mid-way process is to French polish the case, and then part strip it, using methylated spirit on a cloth, and then wax finish on top. All these types of finish will really need some practice, and individual preference will be the biggest factor in deciding how to finish the case, together with the type of wood involved.

With barometers having light inlays or stringing, you may find it very handy to cover them over with a single coat of polish before staining the barometer. This enables them to stay different and not blend in with the case, although they may need toning down first. A coat of polyurethane applied with a good thin brush and a very steady hand will be quite suitable if using spirit-based stains. With oil or water-based stains, a coat of Button polish will normally suffice but, if in doubt, first try out on a little piece of scrap.

The head of a barometer and the acute angles can be difficult to pad, so a good brush is essential when polishing in here, going over with a pad wherever possible. The applied swan-necks on the heads of early barometers were often made of ebony, then of mahogany stained black, but soon makers gave up colouring altogether. These little carved pieces do look most attractive coloured black.

First stain the wood black and then build up with several brush coats of black polish, cutting back between every coat and occasionally using a small pad and also to the small platform upon which the finial sits (*Fig.* 5.3).

The Door

The catches which secure the door are normally just turn catches which are nailed or screwed on. There is a small cut-out place to put your finger in to open the door and the hinges are normally ½ — ¾ in long. Earlier barometers normally have nice cast hinges (*Fig.* 5.19) while mid- to late Victorian barometers onwards often have cheaper pressed brass hinges; both types are available new from parts suppliers.

6

Reassembly of a Wheel Barometer

After removing all the fitments from a barometer and cleaning them as necessary, repairing the case, removing and refilling the tube with mercury, the final stage is to reassemble the whole barometer. It is probably the most satisfying job to do; the process of reassembly can be thoroughly enjoyable, particularly when one ends up with a barometer fit to enhance any house.

Fitting Dial and Rack

Start by placing the case face up on the stand, and secure the dial with the word 'Change' (which is usually 28.5in) in the 12 o'clock position. This will normally mean using the same holes as before but very occasionally the dial may have been incorrectly fixed at a few degrees left or right; you must then decide whether to correct or leave as original. These fixing holes sometimes need plugging with small pieces of pine glued into position.

The screws you use will probably depend on the type of barometer; many late Victorian barometers of poor quality only use steel domed top nails throughout. These usually rust and are not reusable even if desired. Small, countersunk slotted brass screws, size 2 × ⅜in or 1 × ⅜in, are useful for the later Victorian styles onwards, but for any barometer of 1840 and before, particularly of reasonable quality, blued steel screws of the same size are more authentic and look better. Blueing your own screws will give the variation of colour often found on earlier barometers. It is usually only the better-quality mid- to late Victorian barometers that have uniform deep blued screws throughout. If at all possible, it is of course best to reuse the original screws and this should always be the first priority.

To blue your own screws, select some of a suitable size and hold with pliers; rub along sandpaper on a piece of wood in the direction of the slot. Alternatively, hold the screw in a small metal vice and file across the head until quite clean. The graining lines so made will also give an older appearance to the screw. Next, hold the screw in the outer edges of the flame of a gas blow torch or, for a more even colour, place in fine sand or brass filings and heat uniformly until the required colour is reached. Some practice will be needed here to get the exact shade and remove from the heat in time. This can also be done by placing the screws head down on a flat, thick piece of brass and heating uniformly. When a satisfactory colour is reached, remove from the heat and quench in thin oil. The screw can then be used, or cleaned and lacquered to prevent rusting. A blue lacquer will often deepen the colour slightly.

To fit the rack, turn the barometer over and open the door. The original screw holes should be fine to secure the rack. If previously nailed, remember to remove any pieces of nail that might stop a screw going into the right position. It is important here to check the clear movement of the set hand pulley through the dial, and position of the set hand spindle. A slight adjustment might correct a fault allowed to go by previously. Check also that the set key fits the square spindle; if original, it no doubt will but if using a replacement it may need a slight amount of easing with a file to allow the key to seat in position. It is not usually necessary but one sometimes comes across a set key spindle which is very thick and will benefit from filing down a little. Take off an even amount from all sides a little at a time; when satisfied that all is right, fix the rack in position.

Turn the barometer over with the door still open and secure the brass set hand in position over the top of the pulley wheel. The hand is normally just a tapering fit and a firm push on while supporting the back of the rack with the other hand will usually secure it (*Fig.* 6.1). With poorly fitting hands it is sensible to add a drop or two of glue when you are sure it is in the right position. If slack, it is sometimes possible to hammer down the burr around the hole in the set hand to tighten the fit (*Fig.* 6.2). Remember to check that the hand turns 360° without touching the dial as this will cause the silvering to wear in quite a short time. The hand should move parallel to the dial (*Figs* 6.3, 6.4). Close the door; if there is a set key collet and it has been removed or you are fitting a new one, fix this now. It should be just a tight fit but often new ones will need a little glue or packing, just enough to hold firm.

The Level Plate

Using the plate as a template, cut a piece of white or light cream paper and place in the level recess, next the bubble and then the level plate. Using the two holes that are there, secure the level plate which acts as a clamp to the bubble. Fix the top screw first in the original hole and this should hold it sufficiently while the barometer is hung from the ceiling to check the operation of the level. While screwing in the bottom screw, check the level, alter the position of the screw if needed until the bubble is central; this, or course, is nearly impossible as the slightest movement left or right will cause the bubble to move to one side or the other. Sometimes, the level plate is wildly out of level, while the engraved words appear level, and *vice versa*; you will need to decide in this case which position looks the best. Do not discard the level plate just because of this; often it may be better to fill the old screw holes and use fresh fixing holes. The level ring is placed in the recess, a tiny spot of glue or two is put in the recess, not on the veneer, and will hold it in position. Sometimes a piece of stained packing, such as cardboard or veneer, may also be necessary.

The Mirror and Frame

As described in chapter 3, the mirror frame is positioned in the recess with about four spots of glue and some packing to enable the frame to be held by the recess. Two clamps used here to ensure the frame seats fully down may be useful (see *Fig.* 3.5); alternatively, use a weight and some blocks of wood. If done last thing at night, no time will be wasted waiting for it to

Fig. 6.1 Pressing set hand onto pulley mounting.

Fig. 6.2 Hammering down burr for a tighter fit.

63

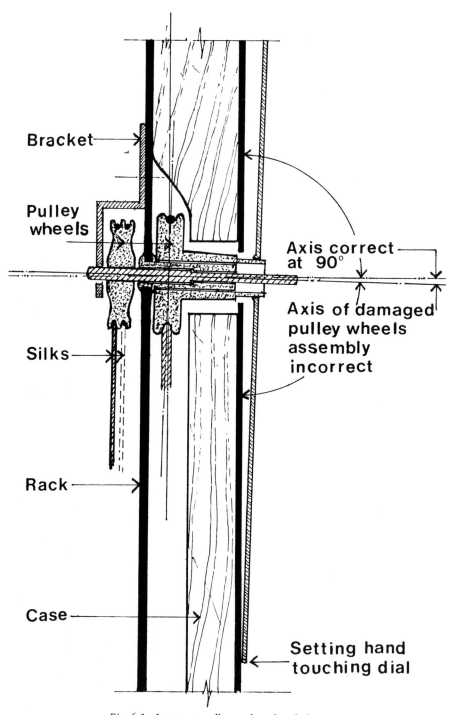

Bracket

Pulley
wheels

Axis correct
at 90°

Axis of damaged
pulley wheels
assembly
incorrect

Silks

Rack

Case

Setting hand
touching dial

Fig. 6.3 Incorrect pulley and set hand alignment.

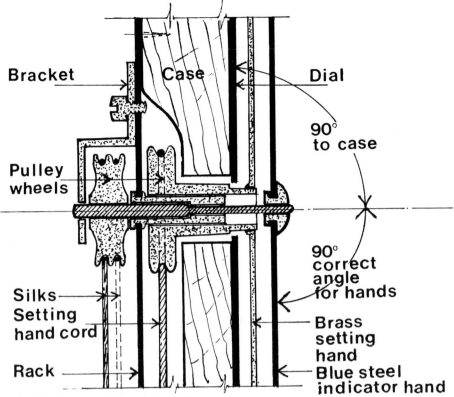

Bracket   Case   Dial

90°
to case

Pulley
wheels

90°
correct
angle
for hands

Silks
Setting
hand cord

Brass
setting
hand

Rack

Blue steel
indicator hand

Fig. 6.4   Correct pulley and hands alignment.

Fig. 6.5   Thermometer bolts, one with spring.

Fig. 6.6   Cutting new spring to size.

dry. On later Victorian rosewood barometers a cast brass bezel is often used. They are generally fitted into the case in the same manner. I have also seen twentieth-century barometers with a very thin pressed brass frame holding a flat mirror by clips behind, fixed onto the case by screws or tacks.

Thermometer Bolt

This assembly (*Fig.* 6.5) is straightforward enough but can still present problems. The spring is placed into the hole and then the bolt; the point of the bolt seats in the open part of the spring and the threaded hole lines up with the knob hole in the case. Screw the knob into the bolt through this hole, but *not tightly*; pressing down the knob moves the bolt in the recess to allow the thermometer box (when fitted) to be removed. If fitting a new thermometer knob and bolt, they will need cutting and filing to fit as necessary; make a point at one end and a chisel-like shape at the other end to catch into the thermometer box. When finally in position, the thermometer bolt is screwed firmly down onto the case. Always take care, if you need to remove the thermometer box, to unscrew the bolt slightly so that it does not scratch the case when you slide it down. Most knobs have a knurled edge to aid gripping. If the spring needs replacing, a new one can be made by stretching out an old Biro spring or similar and wrapping it around a thin metal rod to produce a spring of the required diameter; cut the ends to tidy the spring up (*Fig.* 6.6).

Thermometer Box

This assembly is simple. Place the plate into the box; if a hole is cut for the thermometer bulb to fit, a piece of white or light cream paper is sometimes placed behind the scale. Position the thermometer, place the loops over the glass tube and, with small pliers, pick up the screw that you are using and place into position and screw up with a suitable screwdriver. Some early thermometers have screws which are in fact not threaded but just appear so. They usually respond to screwing in but a drop of glue in each hole will help if not. Mid- to late Victorian thermometers often have round-headed screws and sometimes even nails. Using nails is not recommended as they look cheap and you run the risk of breaking the thermometer tube when hammering them home. Virtually all screws used to fix thermometer tubes were brass. Next, slide the glass into position and refix the end with a slight touch of glue. An elastic band serves admirably to hold it in position until dry (*Fig.* 6.7).

Hygrometer

Hygrometer clips are bent in such a way that once assembled they act as a spring against the hygrometer dial bezel (*Fig.* 6.8). They should seat tidily down against the hygrometer ring and allow it to be removed when the hygrometer clip is pushed downwards against the spring. It is secured by one screw inside the case.

66

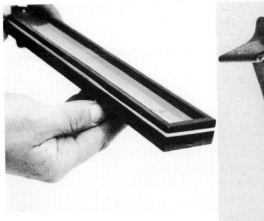

Fig. 6.7 Using elastic band to hold thermometer case until dry.

Fig. 6.8 A new hygrometer clip and one bent ready for use.

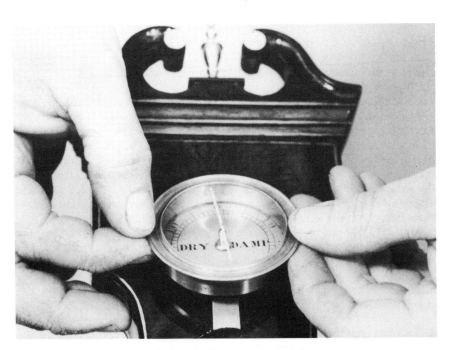

Fig. 6.9 Fitting the hygrometer into the case.

Take care when fitting a new clip not to screw into the recess where the thermometer is fitted from the front as the wood will be very thin just there. Twisting the back of the clip sideways will usually avoid this. The hygrometer should then fit by locating the tab (formed from the dial) into the top of the hygrometer recess and pushing the hygrometer home (*Fig.* 6.9); then allow the clip to position over the bottom edge of the hygrometer.

The Finial

If loose, a small amount of glue to hold may be necessary. If fitting a new finial, then drill a hole central to the head to allow it to be driven home firmly but with sufficient clearance to avoid splitting the wood.

Paterae

These are often found on swan-neck pediments and, when missing, can be turned out of old ivory to fit the size required on the swan-neck. Unfortunately, many replacement paterae are seen overhanging the edges of the scroll because there is little variation in size available, but they can be made to order by some suppliers and, when lightly stained with a brown water stain to show the graining, can hardly be told from old ones — so much more pleasing than plastic!

Now the barometer has taken on its true appearance and little else is left but fitting the tube.

Fitting the Mercury Tube

Now place the barometer face down at an angle on the stand and open the door, position the mercury-filled tube on the left side of the recess when looking at it, and ensure that it fits; on short recesses it may very occasionally be necessary to ease the top or bottom of the tube to allow it to fit if a new tube is being used. Mark where the middle of the tube of the short limb is, just below the bottom edge of the rack, and remove the tube. Using some fine wire cut to about 3 in, twist this around screws of about 2 × ⅜ in and screw into the corner of the case and where you have marked the middle of the short limb.

Replace the mercury tube and secure by fixing the ends of the wire by hand to start, and then by using a small pair of pliers (*Fig.* 6.10). Next, place the guide tube alongside the short limb, clear of the set key pulley, and mark the centre just below the bottom of the rack. Screw another wire here and place a small amount of cottonwool inside the bottom end of the tube with a few drops of glue. Place into position against the wire and tighten. Push the glass down to the bottom of the case and, with a thin stick or rod, push the cottonwool down to the bottom of the case. When the glue dries this will hold the base of the guide tube firmly down but enable replacement to be made easily. Another method of fixing is to use one piece of wire fixed between the short limb and the guide tube, and using this to hold them

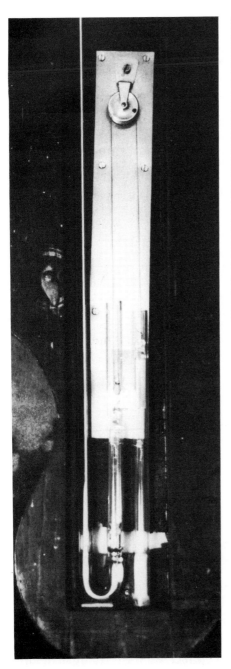

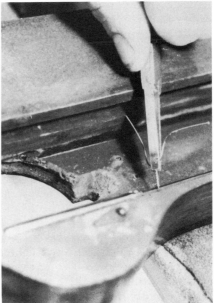

Fig. 6.10 Using pliers to twist wire retaining the tube.

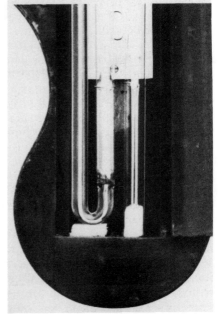

Fig. 6.11 Weights hanging from silks round pulley.

Fig. 6.12 Cards packing the base of the tube for height adjustment.

together, with cork packing between to keep them apart and clear of the set key pulley. Whichever method you use, a neat and tidy job looks best.

It is often useful to fit a plug of stainless steel with cotton thread stuck to one end and a cork which will slide up and down the stainless steel wire (see *Fig.* 4.7). This can be hung inside the case, on a very small hook or cut-off wire staple, ready for use whenever the barometer needs transporting any distance.

With the tube fixed, thread some silk through one hole of the wheel; calculating the size of the hole, tie a knot large enough not to slip through, and cut and pull to meet the wheel and seat in the very small hole with a fine drop of glue. This stops the knot slipping and can easily be removed by a pointed object by a future restorer. Do the same with the other hole and allow approximately 12 in of thread to dangle down. With the back knot on the left at 9 o'clock, and the front knot which is visible to you at 3 o'clock, wind the thread that will be nearest the door twice around the wheel clockwise, and let it hang down. Wind the back thread, the drive thread, twice around the wheel anti-clockwise and let it hang down.

Place the steel spindle into the hole in the rack; the heaviest glass weight should slide comfortably inside the short limb of the mercury tube — tie it so that it rests near the level of the mercury. Then tie the other, lighter weight on the other thread (the counter-balance thread) so that it is near the top of the guide tube (*Fig.* 6.11), then screw the wheel bracket into position, checking that the spindle is at right angles to the dial and moves easily.

On most racks there are two locating pins which avoid incorrect positioning or moving of the rack, but check in case the wheel does not move freely. If fitting a new tube and weights, the weights may need cutting to length and therefore adjusting the weight of each. It will help if you balance the indicating hand with a drop of glue or filing one end until it is balanced when held with a needle through the centre. The wheel will occasionally need packing with washers so as to restrict its movement backwards and forwards, particularly on cheaper types of rack. This will help prevent the hands tangling or the spindle seizing in the bearings. In extreme cases a drop of good-quality clock oil will often help.

Raise the barometer upright and check that all is functioning correctly. If not, check each item one by one and rectify. Before placing the indicating hand in position, cut some pieces of thick cardboard about $\frac{3}{8} \times \frac{1}{2}$ in and place three or four under the tube (*Fig.* 6.12). These will enable you or a future owner to alter the setting of the barometer very easily. Raising the tube lowers the reading and, conversely, lowering the tube raises the reading. Next, hang the barometer from the ceiling hook again and fix the hand in the correct position as checked against an accurate barometer or the local Meteorological Office. A hand is a taper fit and should push on easily. Ensure that both the indicating hand and the set hand are free to travel 360° without engaging each other, or touching the glass or the dial when fitted. When satisfied that all is in order and the correct reading is recorded, return to the stand.

Bezel

This is fixed almost as the last operation. Position it as originally placed if that can be decided; often, bezels have been removed several times so that it can be difficult to tell where they were when first made. As a guide, look through the front of the bezel square on and try to line up the bezel edge around the circumference of the dial, at the same time covering the dark areas created by the bezel being in one position for many years and not allowing the polish underneath to fade; also bear in mind that the border of veneer between the bezel and the edge of the barometer should be approximately an equal distance all round. It is not always easy to accommodate all of these factors. Finally, decide the best position visually; concentrate on the border between the bezel and the edge of the barometer and the faded or darkened areas, leaving the dial and bezel in the best position possible. With bezels which have a centre set knob mounted, the knob should come in the middle of the dial and cover the centre of the indicating hands.

Bezels are usually fitted with two brass screws, normally round-headed; later barometers sometimes have more screws, and good-quality barometers from around 1870 are found with two or three bolts going right through the case and held with small nuts at the back of the case. Georgian barometers, such as the Sheraton shell type with broken pediments, were often fitted with countersunk steel screws which can be replaced — sometimes made to fit by filing — blued and then lacquered. It will be difficult to find suitable new screws off the shelf. With all bezels which are screwed on it will be usual to fill the old holes, sometimes several, with some thin pine pegs glued in and trimmed. This will ensure secure fitting and more accurate positioning as the new screws will not pull towards old holes.

One more minor operation I like to carry out before the job is finished is to cut two small pieces of cork about ⅛ in thick and stick these to the back of the barometer with a drop of glue. They can be held in position until dry with masking tape. These pieces of cork will stop the barometer from rocking on the hinges and catches that stick out from the back of the case and will also prevent scratches to wallpaper or wall surfaces. Finally hang on the wall. When all the glue is dry and everything has been given a final check over, the restoration of the barometer will be complete.

7

Stick or Cistern Tube Barometers

After some experience of restoring mercurial wheel barometers, graduation to the repair of stick or cistern tube barometers is merely a question of confidence and a little extra knowledge. There is not much difference between the types other than mechanism, and the cleaning and repair of case and fitments are very similar. The main difference will be found with the tube (*Fig.* 7.1). Most bulb cistern types can be cleaned and filled if you have mastered the siphon tube; this applies to the Admiral Fitzroy barometer. With the boxwood cistern there is a little more to understand and repair, but it is really a very sensible and straightforward job.

Boxwood Cistern

Fig. 7.2 shows the typical assembly of a boxwood cistern in parts. *Fig.* 7.3 shows a boxwood cistern tube assembled. It is necessary when assembling the cistern and tube to know a given height. The 30 in mark is normally used, determined from the level of mercury in the reservoir and should coincide with the 30 in mark on the register plates. The cistern should be as large as possible to minimise error in reading at the top of the tube. To remove a boxwood cistern from the glass tube, first remove the paper around the screwed joint by cutting around it with a sharp knife. It should then unscrew. Catch the mercury into a suitable container and drain the rest of the mercury from the tube by gently tapping and shaking the tube downwards. Next, soak the cistern in methylated spirit to soften the glue around the glass. After about half an hour try to slide the cistern off the glass cane; if this is not successful, soak for a further half an hour and try again. With a stubborn cistern you may have to resort to soaking in, or pouring over, very hot water to loosen the glue joint. This is nearly always successful. Once separate, clean away all the glue and cord while soft, and immediately wrap the wet cistern in a cloth to help prevent it drying out too quickly. It is advisable to screw the base on a few threads — not all the way — because the water swelling the wood may distort the cistern and the base may need easing around the threads before it can be reassembled.

Once removed and dry, check that the cistern screws together well, a little candle wax may ease a tight thread. The cistern should screw tightly on the base and form a seal against the leather (see cross-section in *Fig.* 7.4). Replacing the leather is often required and can be done by using a suitable soft piece of thin leather cut to fit snugly into the base. The smooth side inside the cistern is then glued well around the edge and can be held in position by gently screwing the cistern down on to it without distorting it, or by resting a suitably shaped circle of wood inside with a weight on. Make quite sure that no glue squeezes out into the cistern base to interfere with the thread. When dry, try fitting on to the cistern.

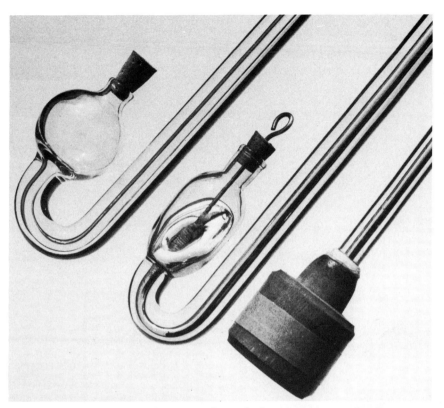

Fig. 7.1 Two bulb cistern tubes and a boxwood cistern tube.

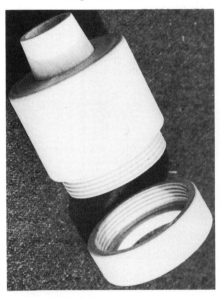

Fig. 7.2 Parts of a boxwood cistern.

Fig. 7.3 An assembled and fitted boxwood cistern tube.

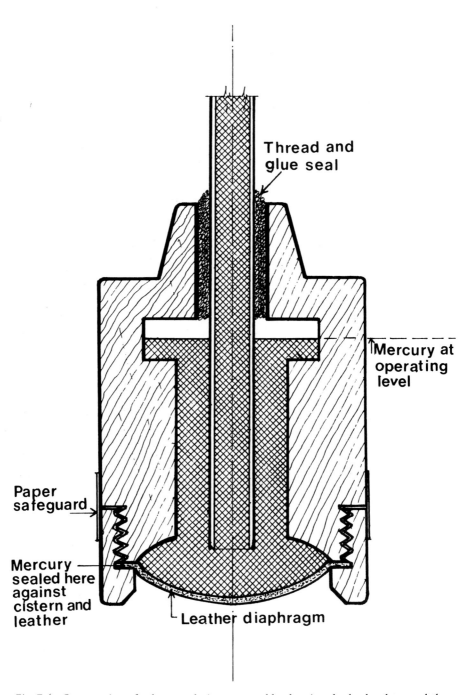

Thread and glue seal

Mercury at operating level

Paper safeguard

Mercury sealed here against cistern and leather

Leather diaphragm

Fig. 7.4   Cross-section of a boxwood cistern assembly showing the leather base and the position of the glass cane.

When ready to glue the glass cane into the cistern, check for the correct measurement into the register plates or case. It will not usually matter if the cane fits further up into the case, unless restricted by the cover or the cut-out on the register plates of course, but must not be short. The cistern should fit so that the level of mercury is at 30 in from the 30 in mark on the register plates. There is usually some leeway for this and, once arranged, can be held firm by packing with suitable pieces of cork. The open end of the glass cane should finish approximately as shown in *Fig.* 7.4.

The cane can normally be cut by running around it at the length desired with a *new* glass cutter or a file and snapping it clean. It is then advisable to smooth and round the end with sandpaper (as shown in *Fig.* 7.5). Take care to hold the open end downwards so as not to foul the inside of the cane with dust and dirt. The very small amount that does enter must be cleaned out with a fine piece of tissue or similar. This rounding off serves two purposes. First, the leather when screwed up tightly, often too tightly, will not be cut by a rough piece of glass and, secondly, any bubbles of air will be very unlikely to enter the tube or get caught round the open end of the tube as they will be encouraged to run away from it up the glass.

Next, cement the glass cane into the decided position. Roughen the cane with sandpaper approximately ¼ in above the cistern and downwards for about 1 in. Coat this area around with glue. Animal glue is normally used, but if you do not use this a good polyvinyl acetate (PVA) glue is suitable. Wrap thick cotton thread around this (*Fig.* 7.5), coat with glue again, and repeat until the desired thickness is obtained to allow the cistern to slide firmly over the cane; a slight twisting action will assist (*Fig.* 7.6). Try in the case for position and angle; when satisfied, wipe the excess glue away and check that no glue has gone into the open end of the cane, and then leave to dry for a few days. When dry, brush or wipe more glue around the joint of the cistern and cane to ensure it is mercury tight (*Fig.* 7.7).

To fill the tube and cistern, insert a catheter tube and hold the tube upside down. Fill with mercury while withdrawing the catheter tube and take care near the end, making sure that the tube is completely full up, and then you can remove the catheter tube from the syringe and fill the cistern with mercury just from the syringe. A steady hand will be needed and the use of a stand is advised. Ensure that any spillage can be suitably dealt with. You will normally need to fill the cistern as much as it can hold, but the amount may need to be less according to the position and size of the cistern on the tube. Now screw the base on and check the reading. It will generally be found that the leather bag, if newly fitted, will drop a little in time and so a slightly higher reading is acceptable to compensate for this. Stretching the leather with a smooth, blunt, rounded piece of wood before assembly may also be necessary.

When satisfied with the reading by comparison with another barometer, cut a strip of brown paper about ½ in wide and glue it over the threaded join (*Fig.* 7.8), making sure that it is securely fixed and filled with glue around the edges. No glue should be used on the threads.

Frequently, boxwood cisterns leak, or have leaked over the years, sometimes through knots or small fissures in the wood. If these are apparent, scrape a small area clean around them and seal well with glue. Remember to leave the top of the cistern clean for the pores of wood to allow air pressure to act on the mercury inside the cistern.

Fig. 7.5 Wrapping thread over glued area of cane: note the rounded end.

Fig. 7.6 Fitting cistern onto glass cane.

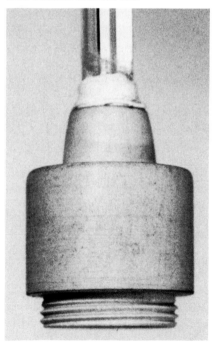

Fig. 7.7 The fitted cistern.

Fig. 7.8 Paper glued over threaded join.

76

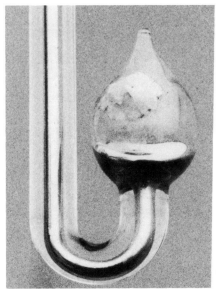

Fig. 7.9   Bulb or bottle cistern tubes.

Fig. 7.10   Paper glued over hole in bulb cistern tube.

Bulb Cistern

Cleaning and refilling the bulb or ball cistern (see examples in *Fig.* 7.9) is a similar job to the siphon tube. When completed, glue a piece of paper over the small side pinhole (*Fig.* 7.10) to help to stop wasting mercury when carried too flat or in very low air pressures. A small pinprick may be necessary to admit satisfactory access by air pressure. With bulbs having cork neck openings, a stainless steel plug, similar to that used with the siphon tube but much shorter, can sometimes be used if the case has sufficient room, otherwise just press a cork in for transport (see *Fig.* 7.1). Remember to remove this cork and just rest it lightly over the hole (to stop dust entering) when setting the barometer up again.

Verniers

Verniers are often fitted to stick barometers and allow more accurate reading, sometimes to within $^1/_{100}$ in. There are two types of these: the rack and pinion vernier operated by a key (*Fig.* 7.11) and a manual vernier (*Fig.* 7.12). Manual ones seldom have problems, although new parts may be needed or the securing spring tightened to stop the vernier dropping. When secured, a little candle wax on the rear of the plate can assist in smoother running. Rack-operated ones may need general repair and sometimes the pinion turns without moving the rack and therefore the two often need bringing closer together.

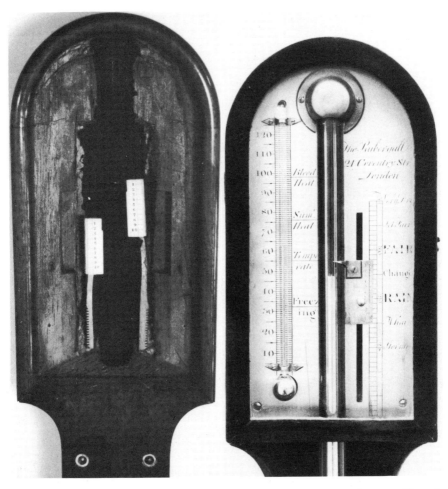

Fig. 7.11 Rack and pinion verniers.   *Fig.* 7.12 Manually operated vernier. Silvered brass dial.

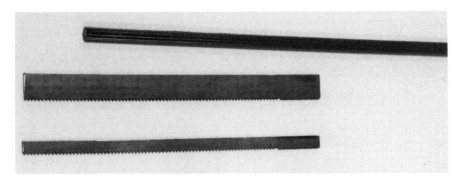

Fig. 7.13 New racks and pinion.

Replacement rack and pinions have either to be specially made to suit one or the other, or replaced in pairs, i.e. a new rack with a matching pinion (*Fig.* 7.13). Access to a metal-working lathe will be needed to turn the pinion down to match the case fitting. The rack will need adapting according to requirement.

Case Repairs

Use the techniques described in chapter 5 for repairing and refinishing the case. A selection of stick barometer pediments is given in *Figs* 7.14—7.22 and cistern covers in *Figs* 7.23—7.34 which may be useful guides if you need to make new items. There are many more styles and inlays often vary. A representative selection of stick barometers is shown in *Figs* 7.35—7.43.

Register Plates

The vast majority of register plates were made of silvered brass (see *Fig.* 7.12), but from around 1780 a few plates were made of painted metal (*Fig.* 7.44), printed paper (*Fig.* 7.45), painted porcelain (*Fig.* 7.46) or ivory (*Fig.* 7.47). Re-silvering brass and cleaning ivory have already been discussed in chapter 3.

Painted metal plates are similar to painted long-case clock dials; they should not be cleaned but can be dusted with a soft brush. If the paint is flaking and peeling get them retouched or restored by an expert artist. Porcelain plates usually have the weather indications and scale painted on in black lettering. Dust with a soft brush and, if necessary, clean carefully with a damp cloth.

Printed paper plates are glued to the case and should be cleaned in a dry condition. Remove dirt by gently rubbing with a soft gum rubber; do not use an india rubber which tends to remove the paper surface. An alternative is to use a proprietary powder which picks up the dirt without disturbing the paper's surface. Another method is to rub the doughy centre of a white loaf of bread along the surface of the paper; change the lumps as they become dirty or else the dirt may be rubbed in again.

Setting

It is not always possible to adjust stick barometers. As with Admiral Fitzroy barometers, they are usually meant to be read and then compensated for by adding the necessary difference for sea level. However, one alteration that can sometimes be made is by adding or removing some mercury in the reservoir at the base of the barometer. With the boxwood cistern type this can be done simply by increasing or decreasing the volume of the reservoir by screwing the threaded transporting screw up or down. Not all barometers will function perfectly if screwed up too far, particularly with low pressures, as they may not have enough room inside the cistern for the mercury to rise.

Fig. 7.14 Domed and moulded pediment, c. 1680.

Fig. 7.15 Broken pediment, c. 1765.

Fig. 7.16 Broken pediment, c. 1780.

80

Fig. 7.17 Broken pediment, c. 1830.

Fig. 7.18 Scroll or swan-neck pediment, c. 1770.

Fig. 7.19 Scroll or swan-neck pediment, c. 1830.

Fig. 7.20   Moulded pediment,   c. 1860.

Fig. 7.21   Carved pediment,   c. 1870.

Fig. 7.22   Moulded pediment,   c. 1875.

Fig. 7.23   Open cistern cover with removable top section, c. 1680.

Fig. 7.24   Turned cistern cover, c. 1720.

Fig. 7.25   Hemispherical open cistern cover with removable top section, c. 1760.

Fig. 7.26   Turned cistern cover, c. 1765.

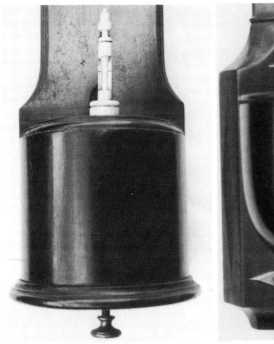

Fig. 7.27   Round cistern cover with ivory float,   c. 1770.

Fig. 7.28   Urn-shaped cistern cover,   c. 1805.

Fig. 7.29   Hinged box-shaped bulb cistern cover,   c. 1800.

Fig. 7.30   Hemispherical   cistern   cover, c. 1780.

Fig. 7.31 Shallow turned cistern cover, c. 1830.

Fig. 7.32 Shallow turned cistern cover, c. 1860.

Fig. 7.33 Shallow square cistern cover, c. 1865.

Fig. 7.34 Carved cistern cover, c. 1875.

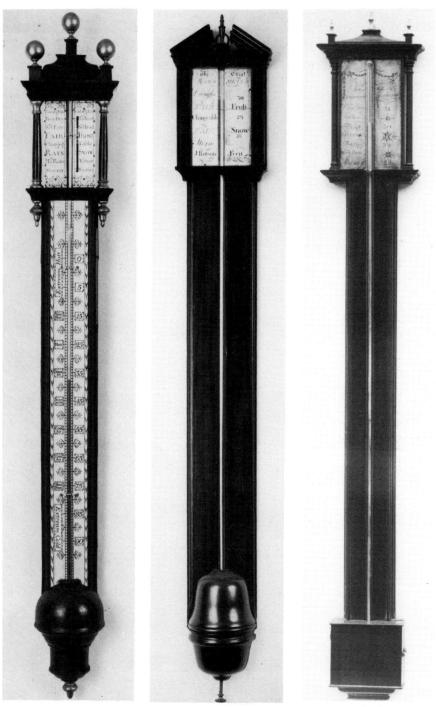

Fig. 7.35 (left)   Moulded case with turned cistern cover and Royal Society Scale thermometer, c. 1720.   *Fig.* 7.36 (centre)   Broken pediment with turned cistern cover, c. 1760.   *Fig.* 7.37 (right)   Pillared hood with square cistern cover,   c. 1810.

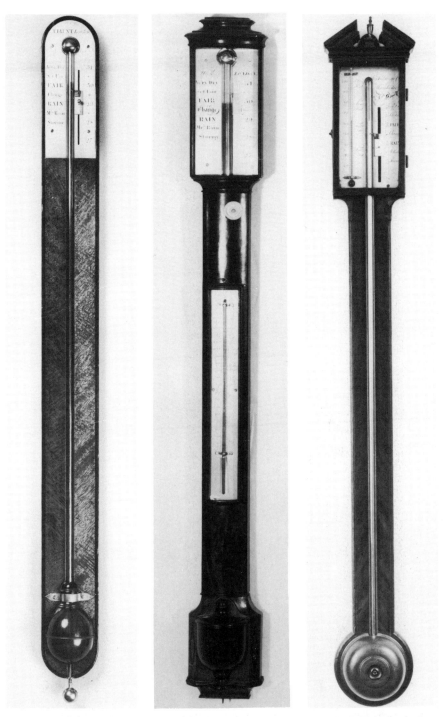

Fig. 7.38 (left) Round top with egg-shaped cistern cover, c. 1810. *Fig.* 7.39 (centre) Bow-fronted case with urn-shaped cistern cover, c. 1820. *Fig.* 7.40 (right) Broken pediment with shallow turned cistern cover, c. 1830.

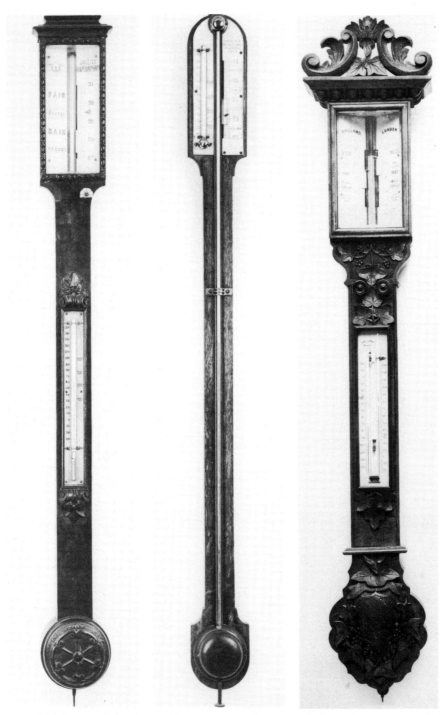

Fig. 7.41 (left) Moulded and carved barometer, c. 1860. *Fig.* 7.42 (centre) Round top model barometer, c. 1875. *Fig.* 7.43 (right) Heavily carved barometer, c. 1875.

Fig. 7.44 Painted metal register plates.

Fig. 7.45 Printed paper register plates.

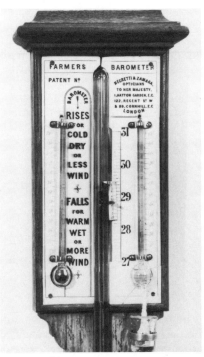

Fig. 7.46 Porcelain register plates.

Fig. 7.47 Ivory register plates.

Transporting

Take care when carrying stick barometers. Bulb cistern stick barometers should never be laid flat but as a general rule laid at an angle of about 40°. While the boxwood cistern tubed barometer was designed for its great ease of transportation — it may well be perfectly alright flat or perhaps better upside down — if there is a small hole or damage anywhere further problems may ensue. There will usually be a threaded screw at the very bottom of the boxwood cistern case. Sometimes it is necessary to use the vernier key to operate this. If moving the barometer for any appreciable distance, it is advisable to screw up this thread until the mercury fills the top of the tube and you meet some resistance on the screw. If you screw too far or too hard you run the risk of tearing the leather diaphragm at the base of the cistern which may be perished slightly with age and you could find yourself with mercury over the floor, so *take care*.

As recommended for wheel barometers, whenever moving any mercurial barometer enclose at least the bottom half in a polythene bag with no holes in to ensure that any possible spillage is immediately contained. Again, if travelling by car, carry the barometer across the car to reduce the possibility of the mercury surging when braking.

Admiral Fitzroy Barometer

The Admiral Fitzroy is a curious and popular style of barometer (*Figs* 7.48 and 7.49). Care should always be taken when carrying it. If it has a plugging device, this should be fitted while holding the barometer at an angle (the tube filled at the top). When plugged, still refrain from carrying it upright as the weight of mercury is constantly trying to force past the plug and with time and shaking may well do so. Always transport, whether plugged or not, at an angle of about 40°.

Most repairs to Admiral Fitzroy barometers are straightforward. Perhaps a mention of the storm bottle would be useful. When the solution is missing the bottle can be refilled, using one of the recipes available, and sealed again. The following recipe is probably the most suitable for cost, effect and availability.

For chemical weatherglass or storm bottle:

> 2 drams camphor
> ½ dram potassium nitrate
> ½ dram ammonia chloride dissolved in 2 fl oz absolute alcohol
> 2 fl oz water

90% alcohol may be acceptable and it may be necessary to increase the quantity of water to ensure a suitable precipitation of the camphor crystals.

There are some interesting predictions which are supposed to be possible, some of these are:

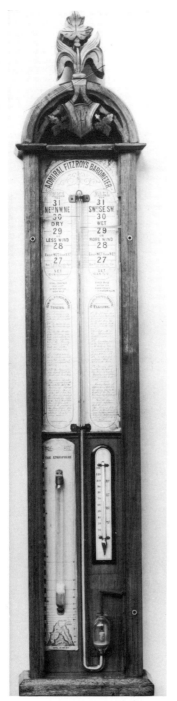

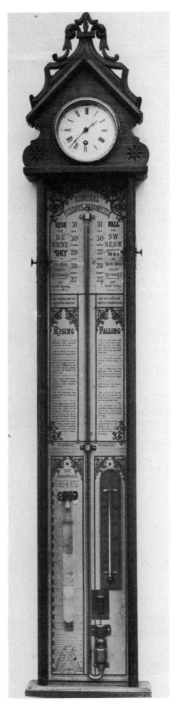

Fig. 7.48   Admiral Fitzroy's barometer, c. 1875.

Fig. 7.49   Admiral Fitzroy's barometer, c. 1885.

Clear liquid: bright weather

Crystals at bottom: thick air, frost in winter

Dim liquid: rain

Dim liquid with small stars: thunderstorms

Large flakes: heavy air, overcast sky, snow in winter

Threads in upper portion of liquid: windy weather

Small dots: damp weather, fog

Rising flakes which remain high: wind in upper air regions

Small stars: in winter on bright sunny days snow in one or two days

The weatherglass is unlikely to have any credibility. The peculiar variations are possibly caused by heat change, light change or even static electrical or ion changes in the immediate area of the weatherglass. Further study of this mixture would be most interesting.

8

Aneroid Barometers

'Aneroid' means 'without liquid', and it was in 1843 that Lucien Vidie, a Frenchman, invented a barometer without using liquid to measure pressure. It was called an 'aneroid' and consisted of a shallow, sealed metallic chamber, almost exhausted of air, with its upper and lower surfaces corrugated in concentric circles to make them flexible. The lower surface was fixed to a base and the sides of the chamber were prevented from collapsing inwards by a spring. The upper surface was in contact with the short arm of a lever and a longer arm operated an index pointer. Changes in atmospheric pressure caused changes in the height of the chamber and so moved the index pointer which was magnified by a lever system.

Fig. 8.1 shows a line drawing of the type of aneroid barometer made by Vidie and sold in London by E. J. Dent in 1849. The sealed metallic chamber DD is prevented from collapsing by the two supports BB, the lever CC and the helical or spiral spring S. Changes in air pressure raise or lower the lever CC which is connected to levers 1, 2 and 3. A fine watch chain connects the end of lever 3 to the spindle of the indicating hand and a hair spring keeps the watch chain taut.

Various improvements were made to the efficiency of the aneroid barometer during the 1850s. A curved spring replaced the spiral one and thought was given to corrections in the readings required as a result of changes in temperature. Two systems were adopted.

The first involved the use of a bi-metallic link in the mechanism, using a combination of brass and steel, while the second system left a small quantity of air or gas in the metallic chamber; both systems would compensate for the effects of heat and cold on the instrument. There was a need to counteract the expansion and contraction of the various metals used for the mechanism and the effect of temperature on the elasticity of the small portion of air in the chamber. Compensation had to be by trial and error and not all barometers were adjusted to the same standard. The bi-metallic link system was achieved by filing away half the thickness of the main lever or arm and replacing the brass removed by an equal amount of steel.

The improvements can be seen in *Fig.* 8.2, showing the mechanism of a barometer c. 1865, and *Fig.* 8.3, a modern reproduction. The corrugated shallow metal chamber can be seen and above it a powerful curved spring resting on gudgeons fixed to the frame; the spring suspends the vacuum chamber. A lever, attached to the top edge of the spring, is connected to a second lever attached to the frame; a pin from this lever is connected to a watch chain, the other end of which is coiled round, and fastened to, the spindle. The indicating hand is fixed to the spindle which also has a hair spring attached to keep the chain taut.

At the same time as Vidie was developing his aneroid barometer, another French engineer, Eugene Bourdon, was working on a similar type of instrument. Bourdon's barometer consisted of a flattened tube of metal, exhausted

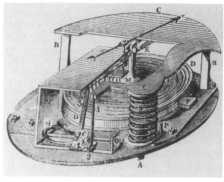

Fig. 8.1 Mechanism of Vidie aneroid barometer, c. 1850.

Fig. 8.2 Mechanism of Vidie barometer, c. 1865.

Fig. 8.3 Reproduction Vidie barometer.

Fig. 8.4 Vidie vacuum chamber with Bourdon mechanism, c. 1900.

completely of air, and curved round to make almost a circle, having an elliptical cross-section. With a change of air pressure the flat evacuated tube curled or uncurled slightly; one end of the tube was fixed to the frame, with the other end free, so that changes in the distance between the two ends could be magnified by a lever system connected to an indicating hand.

In 1849 Bourdon registered a very comprehensive patent covering his invention, including various constructions of the flattened tube, curled in one plane, coiled into a helix or twisted.

A barometer which uses the Vidie evacuated chamber with the Bourdon system of levers and rack and pinion is illustrated in *Fig.* 8.4. It has an open card dial of 3in in diameter and originally had a millimetre scale with Spanish weather indications, but the latter have been covered by a silvered brass ring with English weather indications.

Fig. 8.5 shows a Bourdon barometer made c. 1865. The flattened tube, with a diameter of 3½in, extends to the greater part of a circle. There is an intriguing linkage of levers and counterpoises, terminating in a rack and pinion in order to translate the movement into terms of a moving hand over a dial.

Although the Bourdon type of aneroid barometer was originally more popular that the Vidie instrument in France, it was soon found to be less accurate and sales rapidly declined, both in France and elsewhere, with the result that they are now quite rare in the United Kingdom.

Early aneroid barometers were generally housed in brass cylindrical cases of varying sizes, with a hanging ring, but oak or mahogany stands, often carved, could be purchased separately for use on desks or in halls and libraries (*Figs* 8.6, 8.7). Barometers for use at sea were often made with round, carved wood cases which could be hung on the wall. Later, oak and mahogany banjo-shaped cases were produced, intentionally to imitate the more expensive wheel mercury barometers, and many were identical in shape and size (*Figs* 8.8—8.11).

Aneroid dials were made of metal or silvered metal, but those made for use at sea had enamelled card, glass or porcelain dials to prevent corrosion from salt. A thermometer was often fitted to the dial of an aneroid, and a compass was occasionally attached to the reverse side of the small pocket- or watch-sized traveller's barometer (*Figs* 8.12—8.15). Surveyor's and mining engineer's aneroids were fitted with magnifiers which rotated on a revolving ring (*Fig.* 8.16).

The barometer is set to indicate true barometric pressure when read at sea level (0° altitude). If it is to be used above sea level it must be corrected to give the true sea level reading by using a screwdriver to turn the small screw, seen through the back of the case; this moves the black indicating hand. The following table gives the correct adjustments. For higher altitudes add 0.05 in or 2 mb per 50 ft (1 millibar = 0.0295 in).

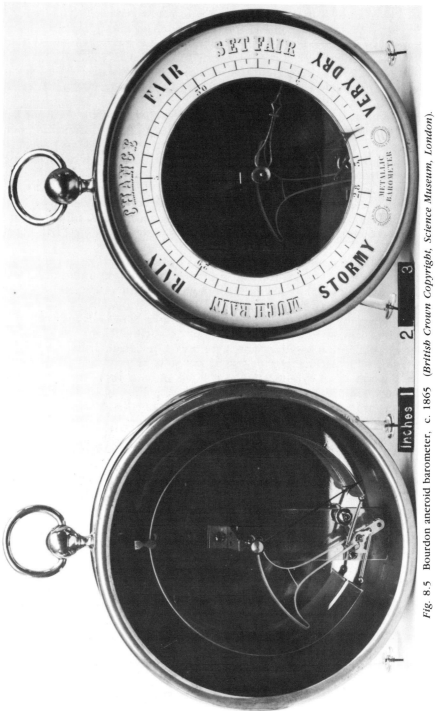

Fig. 8.5 Bourdon aneroid barometer, c. 1865 (British Crown Copyright, Science Museum, London).

Fig. 8.6   Glazed card dial barometer with table stand, c. 1865.

Fig. 8.7   Open dial barometer with table stand, c. 1865.

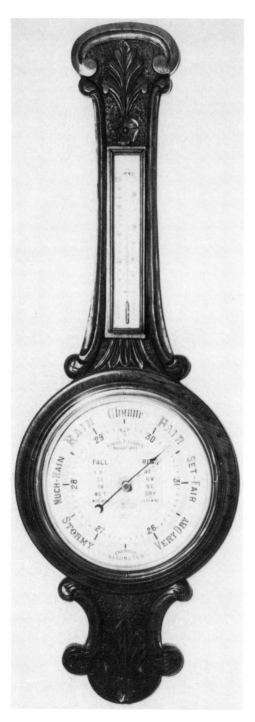

Fig. 8.8 Moulded and carved barometer, c. 1865.

Fig. 8.9 Carved architectural barometer, c. 1875.

98

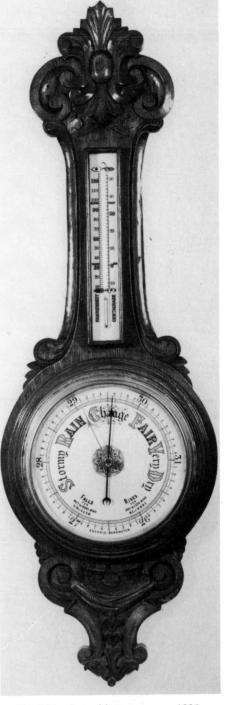

Fig. 8.10 Carved scroll barometer, c. 1875.   *Fig.* 8.11 Carved barometer, c. 1895.

Fig. 8.12 Travelling set in double opening morocco case, c. 1915.

Fig. 8.13 Watch-sized barometer with silvered brass dial in leather case, c. 1870.

100

Fig. 8.14 Watch-sized barometer with enamel dial, c. 1865.

Fig. 8.15 Watch-sized barometer in hunter case, c. 1870.

Fig. 8.16 Pocket-sized surveyor's barometer with magnifier and leather case, c. 1870.

Altitude (ft)	Adjustment (in)	Altitude (ft)	Adjustment (in)
50	Add 0.06	550	Add 0.59
100	" 0.12	600	" 0.64
150	" 0.17	650	" 0.69
200	" 0.22	700	" 0.74
250	" 0.27	750	" 0.79
300	" 0.33	800	" 0.84
350	" 0.38	850	" 0.89
400	" 0.43	900	" 0.94
450	" 0.48	950	" 0.99
500	" 0.54	1000	" 1.04

Aneroid barometers are always set to give the correct reading in an upright or hanging position, and a slightly different reading will be obtained if it is taken when the barometer is face upwards. One way of checking whether an instrument is in working order is to move it from a vertical to a horizontal position and see if there is a slight movement in the indicating hand. Another way is to place it in a transparent plastic bag and then blow up the bag as if to burst it; at the same time observe the indicating hand, through the plastic, to see if it indicates an increase in pressure.

Unlike the mercury barometer, the aneroid can be moved and transported without difficulty. It should be hung or placed in a cool position, of even temperature, away from the sun, fires, radiators, damp and draughts. If handled with reasonable care it is unlikely to need any attention, but it should be checked with a mercury cistern barometer once a year, just to check that it remains accurate.

If the barometer is not working, it is usually for one of the following reasons. The seal on the evacuated metallic chamber may have perished, or the chamber itself may have corroded and allowed air to enter. The linkage between the chamber and the indicating hand may have corroded. Finally, the centre arbor or spindle may have been bent or curved.

It may be possible to ease the linkage corrosion with a proprietary oil, or straighten the spindle, but the metallic chamber would probably have to be replaced and this should be left to a professional instrument repairer. All the other parts can be replaced but this may prove to be expensive and it may be cheaper to fit a reconditioned or a completely new movement. However, if the barometer was made by a well-known maker, every effort should be made to retain as much of the original movement as possible.

Treat any restoration of metal and wood as described in previous chapters. If in good working order, the only attention an aneroid needs is an occasional polish with a soft cloth. Like the wheel barometer, the aneroid reacts slowly to gradual changes in pressure and it should be tapped gently before taking a reading.

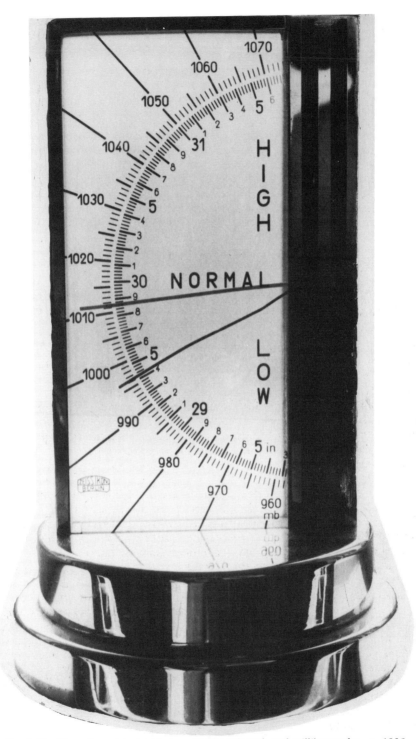

Fig. 8.17 Chromium-plated table barometer with inch and millibar scales, c. 1935.

9

Barographs

The operation of the barograph is similar to that of the barometer, as the sole function of both is to indicate the changing pressure of the atmosphere, from which the probable changes in the weather can be forecast.

The main advantage of the barograph over the barometer is that it records, by a pen mechanism, a continuous graph of the air pressure so that trends can be easily established. The day of the week and the time of day can also be seen from the chart.

In 1663 Christopher Wren suggested to Robert Hooke that he made a 'Weather Clock' and it was completed in 1679. Alexander Cummings made a magnificent barograph clock for George III in 1765, but it was not until 1857 that Admiral Sir Alexander Milne designed a self-recording mercurial barometer which was used as a prototype by commercial manufacturers.

Fig. 9.1 gives a diagrammatic illustration of a modification of Milne's barograph made in 1864. It comprises a large diameter siphon tube, with a counterpoised float attached to a chain passing over a wheel carrying a recording pencil which, by suitable mechanism, is brought once every hour in contact with ruled paper, mounted on a drum revolved by clockwork. The clock is re-wound when a fresh chart is attached to the cylinder, which can be daily, weekly or monthly, according to construction, and the series of dots impressed upon the chart shows the height of the mercury every hour.

A barograph clock, based on the modified Milne design, is illustrated in *Fig.* 9.2. The case is of oak and the thermometer has Fahrenheit and centigrade scales. The clock has an anchor escapement with a pendulum and fusee movement; it was made by Joseph Casartelli around 1870.

The first aneroid barograph was made by Breguet of Paris in 1867, and in the early 1870s barographs similar to the one shown in *Fig.* 9.3 were being produced in England. It consists of an aneroid barometer and an eight-day pendulum clock, each with 8 in dials; between these are placed, in a vertical position, a cylinder with paper attached to it, ruled to coincide with the barometer scale.

Near the paper, a pencil guided by a metal rod is moved up and down as the variations in the atmospheric pressure act upon the vacuum chamber of the aneroid barometer. At every hour, the pencil is made to mark the paper by a mechanism connected to the clock. By this means, a black dotted line is produced showing at a glance the pressure of the air, whether it is rising or falling, for how long it has been doing so and at what rate the change is taking place.

A smaller and more efficient barograph was developed towards the end of the nineteenth century, as illustrated in *Fig.* 9.4. It operates on the same principle as the aneroid barometer in that the expansion and contraction of a series of vacuum chambers, with internal springs, are transmitted by levers to a pointer. The pointer has a pen arm attachment which moves over

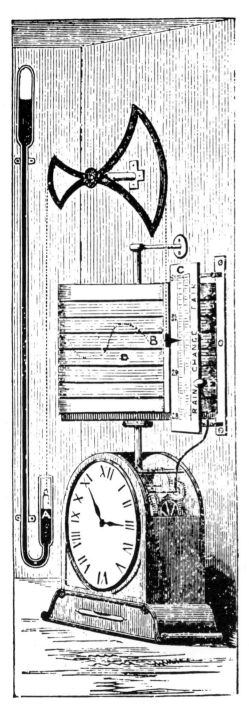

Fig. 9.1 Modification of Milne's mercury barograph, c. 1864.

Fig. 9.2 Mercury barograph clock, c. 1870 (*Peter D. Bosson, Wilmslow*).

105

Fig. 9.3   Self-recording aneroid barometer, c. 1875 (*Dreweatt Watson & Barton, Newbury*).

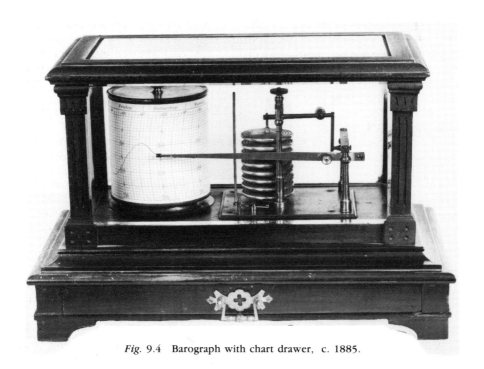

Fig. 9.4   Barograph with chart drawer, c. 1885.

a chart wound round a drum which, activated by clockwork, rotates round its vertical axis once every seven days. The pen leaves behind it a continuous visual record of all pressure changes and the record produced is called a 'barogram'.

Most barographs are compensated for temperature to some extent, but it is important that they should not be exposed to direct sunlight or heat. In order that corrections can be made for changes in temperature some are fitted with a thermometer, whilst a few have a bi-metallic temperature recorder, called a 'thermograph' (*Fig. 9.5*).

The mechanism consists of a strip of two metals with different thermal expansions; these metals are brazed together to form one strip and then coiled into a helix, one end of which is counterbalanced. An increase or decrease in temperature causes the helix to coil or uncoil and so raises or lowers the pen arm, which is positioned behind the barograph pen arm and operates slightly in front of it. There is a round aperture in the glass so that the internal and external temperatures are the same. The chart on the drum records pressure and temperature and is called a 'Baro-Thermo Recorder'.

On all barographs there is friction between the pen and paper which impairs accuracy, and around 1920 a refinement in the form of a 'gate suspension' was introduced to improve sensitivity. This can be seen on the barograph in *Fig.* 9.6; the recording pen is V-shaped and is attached to a very light arm provided at the far end with the gate suspension.

This consists of a two-point bearing tilted slightly so that the line joining the two pivots slopes towards the long axis of the instrument. With this arrangement, the pen arm tends to swing inwards under gravity. The pressure of the pen on the paper is therefore controlled by gravity and not by the flexibility of the pen arm. It can be adjusted by altering the tilt of the suspension until the pressure is only just sufficient to keep the pen in contact with the chart, so that the friction between pen and paper is reduced to a minimum. If the pen trace is 'stepped' rather than continuous the pen pressure on the chart is too great.

The faults that occur with barographs are similar to those experienced with aneroid barometers, with the addition of problems relating to the pen arm. As for aneroids, the correction of minor faults can be attempted but major items should be left to a professional instrument repairer. All the parts can be replaced.

The barograph needs little attention other than changing the chart and inking the pen. Excessive use of ink should be avoided and care should be taken to ensure that none spills on to the pen arm as it will become corroded. The bearings should occasionally be lubricated with a little clock oil, and the gate suspension should be examined from time to time to check that the pen is resting very lightly on the paper. The pen should be washed occasionally with water or methylated spirit.

The clock drum is designed to make a complete rotation in a little over a week, and the chart is printed to make a seven-day record starting on Sunday or Monday. When changing the chart the following points should be remembered.

Move the pen away from the chart by using the pen lifter. Remove the drum from the spindle, loosen the clip and remove the completed chart. Then, wind the clock and adjust the regulator if necessary. Clean the pen,

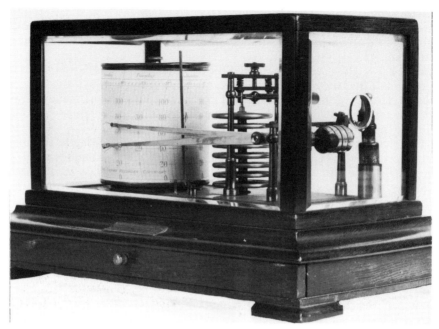

Fig. 9.5   Thermobarograph,   c. 1890.

Fig. 9.6   Portable barograph with gate suspension,   c. 1920.

108

Fig. 9.7   Barograph with circular scale and aneroid type additional dial, c. 1925.

if necessary, and then ink it. Fit a new chart on the drum, making sure that the lower edge is touching the flange at the base of the drum, and that the end of the chart overlaps the beginning and not *vice versa*. Place the drum on the spindle and let the point of the pen nearly touch the chart before adjusting to the correct time, by turning the drum backwards. Using the pen lifter, let the point of the pen touch the chart. Finally, examine the chart to make sure that the pen has begun to write.

On most barographs the pen can be adjusted to any vertical position on the chart by means of a milled-head screw generally positioned above the bank of vacuum chambers.

Meteorological Office barographs often have the addition of a time marker; it is fitted to the top of the case and, when depressed, it raises the pen to make a vertical line. This is for recording purposes and the marks should be made at the same times each day.

The barograph requires careful handling, particularly in cleaning and lubricating, as it is a delicately balanced instrument.

Appendix I

Tools and Equipment

Restorers will often build up a large selection of tools over the years and work from a nucleus of favourite ones. Apart from the obvious smaller tools required, such as a small screwdriver, a hammer, pliers and so on, the following will often prove extremely useful.

> Barometer stand (see *Fig.* A2 for construction)
> Mercury bench (see *Fig.* A3 for construction)
> Scratch stock to enable copying of mouldings
> Set of needle files
> Adjustable block plane for fine veneer work
> Purfling tool for inlaying stringing
> Small gouges
> Piercing saw and blades
> Stanley knife and blades
> Spring extractor (see *Fig.* A1)
> Very fine knife blade for getting under dials
> Soldering iron
> Long-nosed pliers
> Round-end pliers
> Vacuum box for creating a vacuum
> Syringes and catheter tubes
> Feathers, with a rubber tube holder
> Small hand drill
> Small pointed bradawl

Appendix II

Formulae and Special Preparations

Brass Cleaning Solution

1 part ammonia (880)
8 parts water
Dash of washing-up liquid

Keep in a tight screw-top container when not in use. To use, submerge all brass items completely for about 20 minutes, then rinse and clean with metal polish and wire wool (000); buff, if required. Some stubborn dirt and corrosion may need longer in the solution but take care not to forget about items left in it! Similar solutions can be purchased from clock material stockists.

Blueing

Possibly the most useful blueing aid for the amateur is a small pot of solid gun blue, for example, G96 Brand by Jet-aer Patterson, New Jersey 07524, USA. This or something similar should be available from gunsmiths and sports shops selling shotguns. The method entails rubbing crystals on to the clean steel (in this case usually a barometer hand) and rinsing, probably several times, to acquire a satisfactory colour.

Another blueing agent is blueing salts available from some clock material stockists. Even more care will be needed when using this as it is used hot and the fumes are dangerous. As with all chemicals and solutions, take great care and follow the manufacturer's instructions.

Silvering Paste

This is basically a heavily laden silver compound which will deposit silver on to clean brass. One such mixture can be made from silver chloride, cream of tartar and salt, but as the mixing needs to be controlled well and the silver content is expensive even professional restorers would be well advised to buy it from a supplier. The silver content of the paste may vary from firm to firm and consequently the price! Always keep away from light in dark, sealed containers.

Polish Reviver

There are many types of polish reviver available from shops and polish suppliers. One reviver that is often effective can be made from equal parts of methylated spirit, pure turpentine (not white spirit or turps substitute) and boiled linseed oil with a few dashes of vinegar (optional). When this is rubbed into some polished surfaces, which are dry and poor, the results can sometimes be surprising. It is best to leave the surfaces to dry before polishing off with a soft cloth and, when completely dry, applying a wax polish.

Mercury Spillage Treatment

Great care should always be taken when handling and using mercury. If you have a spillage or you are concerned about mercury on a floor, then the following preparation should help to 'mop' up the mercury. It is almost impossible to gauge the level of mercury spillage over years in a workshop without the use of a mercury vapour reading instrument. These are very expensive to buy (and not required often) but can sometimes be available from industrial cleaning companies, or the Health and Safety Executive may be able to assist if there is a suspected risk to health from mercury spillage.

Mix 50/50 by volume slaked lime (calcium hydroxide powder) with flowers of sulphur (refined sulphur, yellow), add water and mix into the consistency of single cream or emulsion paint. Pick up from the dry floor as much as you can of the spillage by sweeping well and bagging up the waste.

The use of a vacuum cleaner is not suitable as you will be creating more mercury fumes! Paint the lime and sulphur preparation on to the floor with a large brush, paying particular attention to cracks and crevices. Allow to dry well, possibly over night. Sweep up the dry powder. Repeat if there has been a heavy spillage or the mercury vapour lamp indicates a high amount of mercury. Treat all waste as contaminated and dispose of at a suitable chemical waste deposit (contact your nearest waste disposal office if necessary).

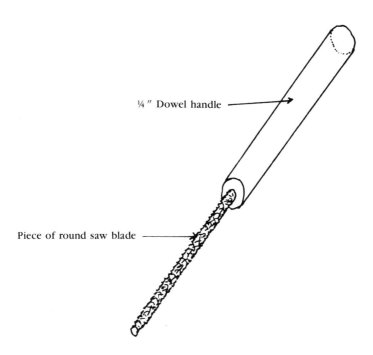

¼ " Dowel handle

Piece of round saw blade

Fig. A1 Thermometer catch spring extractor.

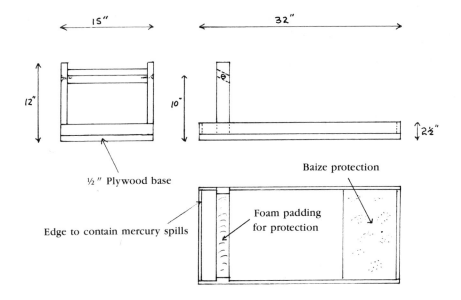

Fig. A2   Construction of a barometer stand.

½ " Plywood base

Edge to contain mercury spills

Baize protection

Foam padding
for protection

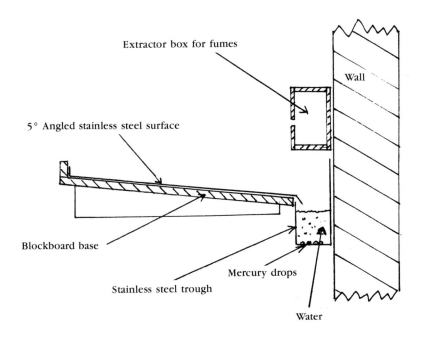

Fig. A3   Bench for use when handling mercury.

Extractor box for fumes

Wall

5° Angled stainless steel surface

Blockboard base

Stainless steel trough

Mercury drops

Water

113

The author with a restored barometer.

Bibliography

Banfield, Edwin, *Antique Barometers: an Illustrated Survey* (Baros Books, Trowbridge, 1989).

Banfield, Edwin, *Barometers: Aneroid and Barographs* (Baros Books, Trowbridge, 1985).

Banfield, Edwin, *Barometers: Stick or Cistern Tube* (Baros Books, Trowbridge, 1985).

Banfield, Edwin, *Barometers: Wheel or Banjo* (Baros Books, Trowbridge, 1985).

Bolle, Bert, *Barometers* (Antique Collectors' Club, 1981).

Goodison, Nicholas, *English Barometers and their Makers 1680—1860* (Antique Collectors' Club, 1977).

McConnell, Anita, *Barometers* (Shire Publications Ltd, 1988).

Middleton, W. E. K., *The History of the Barometer* (The Johns Hopkins Press, Baltimore, 1964).

Thoday, A. G., *Barometers* (Science Museum, London, 1978).

Index